POCAHONTAS, *Seymour*
PONTIAC, *Peckham*
SACAGAWEA, *Seymour*
SEQUOYAH, *Snow*
SITTING BULL, *Stevenson*
SQUANTO, *Stevenson*
TECUMSEH, *Stevenson*

NAVAL HEROES

DAVID FARRAGUT, *Long*
GEORGE DEWEY, *Long*
JOHN PAUL JONES, *Snow*
MATTHEW CALBRAITH PERRY, *Scharbach*
OLIVER HAZARD PERRY, *Long*
RAPHAEL SEMMES, *Snow*
STEPHEN DECATUR, *Smith*

NOTED WIVES and MOTHERS

ABIGAIL ADAMS, *Wagoner*
DOLLY MADISON, *Monsell*
JESSIE FREMONT, *Wagoner*
MARTHA WASHINGTON, *Wagoner*
MARY TODD LINCOLN, *Wilkie*
NANCY HANKS, *Stevenson*
RACHEL JACKSON, *Govan*

SCIENTISTS and INVENTORS

ALBERT EINSTEIN, *Hammontree*
ALECK BELL, *Widdemer*
CYRUS MCCORMICK, *Dobler*
ELIAS HOWE, *Corcoran*
ELI WHITNEY, *Snow*
ELIZABETH BLACKWELL, *Henry*
GEORGE CARVER, *Stevenson*
GEORGE EASTMAN, *Henry*
HENRY FORD, *Aird and Ruddiman*
JOHN AUDUBON, *Mason*
LUTHER BURBANK, *Burt*
MARIA MITCHELL, *Melin*
ROBERT FULTON, *Henry*
SAMUEL MORSE, *Snow*
TOM EDISON, *Guthridge*
WALTER REED, *Higgins*
WILBUR AND ORVILLE WRIGHT, *Stevenson*
WILL AND CHARLIE MAYO, *Hammontree*

...GTON,
Stevenson
CLARA BARTON, *Stevenson*
DAN BEARD, *Mason*
FRANCES WILLARD, *Mason*
JANE ADDAMS, *Wagoner*
JOHN L. LEWIS, *Korson*
J. STERLING MORTON, *Moore*
JULIA WARD HOWE, *Wagoner*
JULIETTE LOW, *Higgins*
LILIUOKALANI, *Newman*
LUCRETIA MOTT, *Burnett*
MOLLY PITCHER, *Stevenson*
OLIVER WENDELL HOLMES, JR.,
Dunham
SUSAN ANTHONY, *Monsell*

SOLDIERS

ANTHONY WAYNE, *Stevenson*
BEDFORD FORREST, *Parks*
DAN MORGAN, *Bryant*
ETHAN ALLEN, *Winders*
FRANCIS MARION, *Steele*
ISRAEL PUTNAM, *Stevenson*
JEB STUART, *Winders*
NATHANAEL GREENE, *Peckham*
ROBERT E. LEE, *Monsell*
SAM HOUSTON, *Stevenson*
TOM JACKSON, *Monsell*
U. S. GRANT, *Stevenson*
WILLIAM HENRY HARRISON,
Peckham
ZACK TAYLOR, *Wilkie*

STATESMEN

ABE LINCOLN, *Stevenson*
ANDY JACKSON, *Stevenson*
DAN WEBSTER, *Smith*
FRANKLIN ROOSEVELT, *Weil*
HENRY CLAY, *Monsell*
JAMES MONROE, *Widdemer*
JEFF DAVIS, *de Grummond and Delaune*
JOHN MARSHALL, *Monsell*
TEDDY ROOSEVELT, *Parks*
WOODROW WILSON, *Monsell*

De Witt Clinton

Boy Builder

Illustrated by Robert Doremus

De Witt
Clinton

Boy Builder

by Mabel Cleland Widdemer

THE **BOBBS-MERRILL** COMPANY, INC.
A SUBSIDIARY OF HOWARD W. SAMS & CO., INC.
Publishers · INDIANAPOLIS · NEW YORK

*For Mrs. Edward Bovel of the Johnstown, New York,
Public Library, with deep appreciation for her always
kind and intelligent help in my research*

*And for dear Pamela and Susan Widdemer, with a
heartful of love*

Illustrations

Numerous smaller illustrations

Contents

Books by Mabel Cleland Widdemer

ALECK BELL: INGENIOUS BOY

DE WITT CLINTON: BOY BUILDER

HARRIET BEECHER STOWE: CONNECTICUT GIRL

JAMES MONROE: GOOD NEIGHBOR BOY

PETER STUYVESANT: BOY WITH WOODEN SHOES

WASHINGTON IRVING: BOY OF OLD NEW YORK

★ ★ # De Witt
Clinton

Boy Builder

A Birthday Cake

It was a hot August day in 1774. Young De Witt Clinton sat on the steps of his home in Little Britain, New York. He watched a bluebird flash across the dark green of the forest which grew near the house. He saw a black ant scurry along, carrying something twice its size.

De Witt sat very quietly for a five-year-old boy. He caught his breath and held it. He must not disturb a yellow butterfly which had alighted on his mother's rosebushes growing near the steps. De Witt Clinton watched patiently all the living creatures about him, because he was interested in nature in any form.

What wonderful sights, sounds, and smells seemed to surround him! It was even baking day. What delicious odors drifted on the air! How good freshly baked bread and pies and cakes smelled! De Witt sniffed like a hound puppy, and his mouth watered.

Mrs. Clinton came to the door. She wiped her hands on her big white apron and smiled down at her young son.

"It's your grandmother's birthday," she said wistfully. "I wish I could send her a birthday cake——" Her voice trailed off for she didn't think there was any possible way to get the cake to her mother.

De Witt scrambled to his feet, his face aglow. "I'll take it to her, Mother!" he cried.

Mrs. Clinton put her hand on his shoulder and said gently, "I'm afraid you are too young to go so far alone, De Witt, but thank you very much for offering to go."

Charles, De Witt's older brother, came whistling up the path from the barn. He had been feeding the chickens. An empty pail swung from his hand. He waved when he saw his mother and brother.

De Witt turned quickly to Mrs. Clinton. "If Charles will go with me, can we take the birthday cake to Grandmother?" he asked eagerly.

Charles joined them and heard De Witt's question. He said, "I'll go with De Witt to Grandmother's, Mother. Wait until I put the pail away, and I'll be right with you."

Mrs. Clinton looked from one to the other of her handsome young sons. Charles and De Witt were tall and well-built and strong for their ages. She was proud of them, and she knew she could trust them. She would let the boys go, for she did want to send her mother the birthday cake.

"I'll go and put the cake in a basket," she said. "Thank you both very much. Now you must

13

promise me you will be very careful and not get into any trouble."

"We promise," the boys said in unison. They smiled at each other as their mother disappeared into the house. How often she had given them that warning.

"Let's cut through the forest instead of going across the fields," Charles suggested later. "It will be shorter and will not be so hot."

"It would be nicer than the hot walk across the fields," De Witt agreed, "but the forest is Indian hunting ground——"

"Come on," Charles said impatiently. "Nobody will be hunting today. It's too hot." He plunged into the forest, and De Witt followed.

The light in the forest was a queer eerie gray. The trees grew so thick that their branches met and tangled overhead. Bushes and vines grew close to the narrow trail. They felt as if they were walking through a long green tunnel.

14

There were odd rustlings and strange sighing sounds. The boys glanced anxiously about. They expected at any moment to see a wildcat or a bear or perhaps even a wolf, for there were many wild creatures in the forest.

"I'm going home across the fields even if it is hot and longer," De Witt announced after a long moaning sound near them had made the boys quicken their steps.

Charles didn't answer, but he walked so fast that De Witt had a hard time keeping up with him. Charles was sorry he had suggested the short cut. He didn't like the strange noises and the eerie light either, but he didn't want De Witt to know he was scared.

Suddenly, ahead of them on the narrow trail, a dark figure stepped from the shadows. The boys stopped. Their hearts pounded against their ribs. A young Indian boy stood in the middle of the path and blocked their way.

Charles and De Witt knew that the white settlers had been having trouble with the red men. Since the war had begun, the British had hired some of the Indians to fight with them against the Americans.

The Indian lad came toward them. He seemed to be about Charles's age. As he drew nearer, they saw that he looked sick and tired. His moccasins were worn and shabby, and his hunting shirt and trousers were stained and torn.

"Thunder Cloud tired and hungry," he said when he reached the boys. "You give Thunder Cloud something to eat? What you have in basket. Let Thunder Cloud see."

Thunder Cloud put out his hand as if to snatch the basket from Charles, but Charles was too quick for him. Charles swung around and tripped Thunder Cloud so that he fell to the ground.

"Run!" Charles shouted to De Witt and started off down the trail.

De Witt did not follow him. De Witt stared down at the Indian boy who lay where he had fallen. Thunder Cloud was too exhausted to get up. He looked up at De Witt with pleading brown eyes.

"Come back, Charles!" De Witt shouted. "He really is tired and hungry."

Charles only beckoned to De Witt and called, "It's a trick! There may be others around! Run while you have the chance!"

"No others around," Thunder Cloud murmured feebly.

"Come back!" De Witt shouted again. "We'll give him Grandmother's birthday cake."

Charles started walking slowly back to De Witt and the Indian boy. He meant to be ready for the Indian if he were playing a trick. If De Witt would not follow him, Charles could not leave him here in the forest.

Charles knew the character of his young

brother well enough to be sure that De Witt would never leave the tired, hungry Indian boy until he had given him something to eat.

"Please give him the cake," De Witt said when Charles reached him.

"I won't!" Charles answered. "It's Grandmother's birthday cake, and we promised Mother we'd take it to her."

De Witt sighed. Charles was right. The cake wasn't their cake to give away. "Maybe Grandmother and Mother wouldn't mind if we gave him just one piece," he said. "You could cut it, Charles. Won't you please?"

Charles looked at De Witt. Charles knew that the only way to get out of the forest was to do what De Witt asked. He put the cake on a flat rock, far enough away so that Thunder Cloud could not make a sudden grab at it. He unsheathed the hunting knife his father had given him for his birthday and started to cut a thin slice.

"That won't be enough," De Witt said. "Give him my share, too."

Charles cut a more generous piece. The Indian boy, who was now sitting up, watched him with hungry eyes.

De Witt brought Thunder Cloud the cake. He grabbed it and began to eat it in big bites.

"I wish we could have given you the whole cake," De Witt said. "But it's our grandmother's birthday, and our mother trusted us to take the cake to her."

"You kind boys," Thunder Cloud muttered. "Thunder Cloud never forget."

"Good-by," the boys said politely. Then they turned and ran away. They ran all the way to the clearing in the middle of which stood their grandmother's house.

She was very glad to see them. They told her of their adventure and how they had given Thunder Cloud a piece of her birthday cake.

"That was good of you," she said. "Now let's eat the rest of it." She placed the cake on a pretty blue plate and poured three glasses of rich foaming milk. How the boys enjoyed it!

De Witt wouldn't take any cake at first. "I gave my share to Thunder Cloud, Grandmother," he explained. He looked a little sad.

"I shall feel very bad if you don't have some," Grandmother De Witt said.

De Witt didn't need much coaxing. The cake tasted wonderful. He hoped Thunder Cloud had enjoyed it as much as he did.

"No more short cuts," Grandmother De Witt said when they were ready to go home. "Tell your mother that was the best birthday cake I ever tasted. Thank you for bringing it."

The Cave

MRS. CLINTON and her children were gathered around the stone fireplace in the family room. Outside the night was the wild kind that sometimes comes in September as a reminder of the coming autumn and winter.

The wind hooted down the chimney and made the yellow and red flames dance and bow. Howling around the house, the wind shook the doors and windows. Inside the house the candle-lighted room was so warm and cozy that none of the Clintons paid attention to the wind.

De Witt was stretched out on the floor before the fireplace. He was trying to read one of the books his fifteen-year-old brother, Alexander, had left when he went off to join the American Army under General Washington. De Witt was having a hard time with some of the longer words. He looked up at his mother and said, "What does f-r-e-e-d-o-m spell?"

Mrs. Clinton dropped into her lap the long gray stocking that she was knitting for her husband, Colonel James Clinton. The stocking was one of several pairs she hoped to be able to send him. He was in Canada with the brave General Montgomery, and she knew it was cold there.

She gave her full attention to her young son and spoke seriously.

"F-r-e-e-d-o-m spells freedom," she told him. "It is a word I hope you will never forget. Your father and brother and General Washington and other brave men like them are fighting for freedom. Freedom is the most cherished possession of the American people. You must never forget

23

how important freedom is to a nation or to a person. We must preserve it."

De Witt spelled it over to himself several times. He made up his mind never to forget it.

Suddenly they heard the sound of hoofbeats over the noise of the storm.

De Witt ran to the window and looked out.

"Who would be out on a night like this?" Mrs. Clinton wondered. She put down her knitting.

"Whoever it is, he's stopping here!" De Witt exclaimed. He watched the rider leap from his horse and throw the reins over the hitching post and hurry to the door.

Three loud knocks brought Mrs. Clinton to her feet. She reached for the gun her husband had taught her to use.

The knocking grew louder. "Open the door, De Witt," she commanded. Her voice sounded calm. She knew she must keep it calm so that the children would not know she was frightened.

She had a feeling that whoever was at the door was bringing bad news.

De Witt drew back the bolt and pushed the iron bar aside. Wind and rain rushed into the house when the stout wooden door swung open.

The candlelight fell on the copper-colored face of an Indian boy. He was wrapped in a rain-soaked blanket.

"Stop where you are!" Mrs. Clinton said sharply. "Why do you come to us on a night like this? It is very late."

The Indian boy threw back his blanket and turned to De Witt. "He know me," he said.

"It's Thunder Cloud, Mother!" De Witt cried. "We told you we gave him some of Grandmother's birthday cake!"

"He good boy," Thunder Cloud said, pointing to De Witt. "He feed Thunder Cloud when Thunder Cloud was hungry. Thunder Cloud never forget kindness."

Mrs. Clinton stepped aside and lowered her gun. "Come inside," she said. "The boys told me about you. Draw close to the fire for you are shivering with the cold."

De Witt closed and barred the big door and turned to Thunder Cloud and his mother.

"Thunder Cloud have no time," the Indian lad said quickly. "Thunder Cloud slip away to tell kind boys family must go and hide. Bad Indians coming to rob and burn white people's homes tonight. You not safe."

"Where can we hide?" Mrs. Clinton asked. The children drew close to her.

"Thunder Cloud will take you to cave. Only Thunder Cloud goes there. Bad Indians afraid. They killed Brown Bear, one of my people, there. They say Brown Bear's spirit stays there. Will do them harm. No spirit. Thunder Cloud spend many nights and days there. No see spirit of Brown Bear. You come quick!"

"Put on your boots and your heavy coats," Mrs. Clinton told her children. "Charles, you carry the gun and ammunition. De Witt shall help me carry blankets and food." She began to gather things together.

Thunder Cloud sprang forward. "No time!" he cried. "Hurry! You come now!" He turned quickly. He snatched a pail of water which stood on a table near a corner, and dashed it on the fire. Then he began to blow out the candles.

"Come now!" he repeated impatiently. He threw wide the door and pushed De Witt and Charles through it. Mrs. Clinton followed with young George in her arms.

It was hard to find their way through the black night. Thunder Cloud led his horse with one hand and grasped De Witt's hand with the other. Mrs. Clinton, with the baby in her arms, stumbled along behind them. Charles came last. He proudly carried the gun and ammunition.

The forest was a frightening place. The trees sighed and bent before the wind. Rain beat down. There were strange noises everywhere.

De Witt was glad to hold on to Thunder Cloud's hand. It gave him courage. Once the Indian stopped and tethered his horse to a broken tree. Cautiously Thunder Cloud led his friends through the dense growth.

They reached the cave at last. Thunder Cloud parted the bushes and vines that hid the cave's entrance from anyone who was not looking for it. They followed him. It was dry and warm inside. The rain and wind could not reach them.

The stone walls twisted and turned. Thunder Cloud led them deep into the blackness. De Witt clung tightly to Thunder Cloud's hand. Mrs. Clinton felt her way carefully along the rough wall with one hand while clutching George tightly in her other arm. Charles stepped carefully along behind her.

Thunder Cloud broke the tense silence. "Stop now!" With his short command he stopped at last and dropped De Witt's hand.

"Won't they see the light?" Mrs. Clinton asked anxiously.

Thunder Cloud shook his head. "No. No see light, but be sure no make fire. Smoke might bring bad Indians. Thunder Cloud return when danger is over."

He slipped away like a bronze shadow. The Clintons were left alone in their forest hide-out.

De Witt looked around the cave. It wasn't a bad hiding place. There was a pile of dry wood in a corner. A blackened circle in the middle showed where a fire could be built. De Witt remembered Thunder Cloud's warning. The candlelight fell softly on their frightened faces.

Mrs. Clinton sank down and eased young George out of her aching arms. He was a large child and heavy.

De Witt and Charles crept back down the long rock passage to the entrance of the cave. They heard the muffled whoops and cries of the Indian raiding party.

They heard the crackling of fire. They saw flames leap higher than the treetops. They heard women screaming and men shouting. They heard the crack of guns. What a night!

The boys crawled cautiously back to their mother. "The Indians are burning everything," De Witt told her.

He looked longingly at the gun which was propped near his mother against the rocky wall. How he wanted to take it and go out and fight the red men who were destroying innocent people's homes!

His mother seemed to read his thoughts. "You are too young now," she said gently. "Someday you may fight for what is right, just as your father and brother are doing."

Despite all the excitement they fell asleep at last. They were all tired out by the wild night's adventures.

The sun was high in the sky when Thunder Cloud returned to tell them they could go home. How different was the walk through the forest in the sunshine and coolness of the day!

The air smelled sweet from last night's rain. Birds sang and little wood creatures ran across the trail ahead of them. It didn't seem possible that the night could have been so horrible. It all seemed like a bad dream.

Mrs. Clinton dreaded to think what they might find when they reached their clearing. Their home might now be but a heap of ashes.

She gave a cry of delight when she saw it standing safe and sound in the bright morning sunlight. The boys shouted and ran toward it. Home had never seemed so dear and safe!

"They saved it!" she said, turning to Thunder

Cloud. Her eyes were filled with tears of happiness and gratitude.

Thunder Cloud struck his chest with a clenched fist. "Thunder Cloud smart Indian!" he told her. "Bad Indians come snooping around. I stay near by. I call out, 'Nothing here to burn!' They no see house in the dark and rain. They believe Thunder Cloud. They go away! Thunder Cloud save house for kind boys and mother."

"Come in, and I'll get breakfast," Mrs. Clinton told him. She felt she could scarcely wait to get her hands on her own familiar pots and pans and stir up a good fire.

What a happy time they had when they sat around the big oak table at last! There were three pitchers of milk and stacks of flapjacks with fresh honey.

"Food never tasted better," De Witt said. He helped himself to his tenth flapjack.

"You'll burst if you eat another thing," his

mother teased him, but she enjoyed seeing her good food disappearing so fast.

"Kind boys have kind mother," Thunder Cloud said when it was time for him to go.

Mrs. Clinton laughed. "Thank you," she said.

De Witt and Charles walked out with Thunder Cloud to where he had left his horse. They had already fed Thunder Cloud's horse.

"You saved our lives and our home," De Witt said as Thunder Cloud swung himself astride the horse. "We'll never forget it."

"Thunder Cloud tell kind boys he not forget when they give him food when Thunder Cloud is hungry," Thunder Cloud answered.

The Indian lad raised his hand in good-by and rode away. Charles and De Witt watched him until he entered the trail into the forest.

"To think he did all that for us just because we gave him a piece of Grandmother's birthday cake!" De Witt said.

A Grandfather's Tale

"If you and De Witt will get me some squirrels I will make a stew for you," Mrs. Clinton told Charles one afternoon.

"May I take the gun with me?" Charles asked. "I'll be very careful." His mother had been giving him lessons on how to handle it since the night Thunder Cloud had warned them about the bad Indians.

"Yes, for I am sure you know how to use it now." Mrs. Clinton nodded. She knew that boys who lived on the frontier in this trying time had to be trusted with guns.

Charles picked it up proudly. "You can carry

the ammunition," he told De Witt. Charles didn't want his young brother to feel left out of things, just because De Witt was only six years old and unable to help much.

"I've got my slingshot, too," De Witt answered. "I'll get a squirrel or two with it."

"Stop in to see how Mr. Green came through the Indian raid," their mother called after them. "You may be able to help him if he had any trouble."

"We will!" they promised. Mr. Green had been a good friend of their Grandfather Clinton. Mr. Green was an old man now. He had lived in Grandfather Clinton's house ever since Grandfather Clinton had died in 1773.

Charles and De Witt liked to visit there, for they knew their grandfather and Mr. Green had been the first to settle in Little Britain many, many years ago. They never tired of the wonderful stories Mr. Green told them.

Mr. Green could tell of the days when Little Britain, New York, had been part of the great wilderness. Mr. Green and Grandfather Clinton had helped hew and carve a settlement out of the forests that still surrounded it.

"Do you think we can talk Mr. Green into telling us a story today?" Charles wondered as they hurried along the forest path.

"Let's get the squirrels before we go into Mr. Green's house," De Witt suggested. "Then if he should tell us a story today, we won't be worrying about any old squirrels for a stew. We can just stay and hear his whole story."

"That's a good idea," Charles agreed. It didn't take them long to bag half a dozen big fat gray squirrels. Charles shot four and De Witt brought down two with his slingshot. They put them in the deep pockets of the hunting shirts they wore.

"I'm going to ask Mother to make me a cap from these skins," Charles said. "My raccoon one she made me two years ago is getting too small for me. I'll give it to you."

"Thank you!" De Witt cried. He was delighted. He had always admired Charles's coonskin cap. How warm it was going to feel this winter when he pulled it down well about his ears. His red knitted cap was nice, too, but it was getting small. Maybe George would soon be able to wear it.

They came in sight of the Fort, which was the nickname for the well-fortified house their Grandfather Clinton had built about 1733. They stopped to admire it as they always did. A stout wood stockade surrounded it. The heavy gates were open now, but they could be closed to protect the people inside from any kind of trouble outside.

"Mr. Green is all right," De Witt said as they walked toward the opened gates.

"Sure," replied Charles. "The Indians would

know better than to try to get the best of anyone in Grandfather's house."

"I bet a lot of people came here for protection the night of the raid," De Witt suggested.

"We could have come, too, if we'd had time," Charles said. "It was just too far away."

Charles and De Witt dashed through the gates and raced across the hard-packed open space before the house. Old Mr. Green was sitting on the front porch. He was whittling and whistling happily.

He looked up and called, "Hi, boys! Come to cheer up an old man?"

They laughed for they knew that was one of his jokes. Mr. Green never thought of himself as being old, and he never needed cheering up. He liked to call himself sixty-four years young, and he had a cheerful disposition. In all the hair-raising experiences and adventures he'd had, he had never lost his sense of humor or his courage.

"Mother asked us to see if you were all right after the raid the other night. She wondered if there was anything we could do to help you," Charles explained.

The old man chuckled. "Doesn't your Ma know by this time that this place has held off so much trouble so many times that nobody even comes near it anymore?"

"I bet some folks came to stay with you," De Witt said. "So they'd be safe, too."

"Some folks?" the old man repeated. "Some mobs, you mean. So many came, that there was scarcely room for a man to stand up straight, let alone sit! It sure was crowded. I missed you and your family. I am glad to see you came through the raid all right."

"An Indian named Thunder Cloud came and warned us just in time. He led us to a cave he knew about. We hid there until morning," De Witt told him. "Then we went home."

40

"We were pretty scared for a time," Charles said. "We could hear the Indians whooping and hollering and see the flames from their fires."

Mr. Green frowned. "Never be afraid, lad," he said. "People smell fear like dogs and wild animals do. Stand up to your enemies and half the time they will turn around and become your friends." Mr. Green wanted to tell about his trip to America on the "George and Anne." "Did you ever hear what happened to your grandfather and me during our trip to America?" he asked.

"No, sir!" the boys said in unison. They looked knowingly at each other. There was going to be one of Mr. Green's good stories.

De Witt and Charles were glad they had the squirrels ready to take home to their mother. Now they could settle themselves comfortably, and they wouldn't have to hurry away before Mr. Green had finished his story. Mr. Green leaned forward and began:

"In the year 1729, King George the Second was King of England. Your grandfather Charles Clinton, for whom you are named—" he broke off to tell young Charles—"decided to take his wife and children to America. He was a wealthy farmer in Ireland where he had been born, and he was a man of culture.

"I was one of his neighbors. I was a lad of eighteen, but I was strong and aching for new adventures. One day your grandfather came to ask my parents if they would become part of the party he was getting together to go with him to America. I overheard them talking. My parents refused, because they had a flock of young ones to bring up.

"I stepped forward and said I'd like to go if your grandfather would have me. Your grandfather said he would be glad to take me along. At first my parents wouldn't give their consent. Finally, I told them I'd run away and go anyway if they refused. They reluctantly gave me permission to go along.

"I joined your grandfather and his family and friends. There wasn't a happier lad in the whole world!"

Then Mr. Green explained that the "George and Anne" left Dublin on May 20, 1729. "That's a date I'll never forget," he said. "Your grandfather had persuaded two of his sisters and their families to join him, besides a company of his friends. All of them had plenty of money and had been able to persuade the Captain to rent his ship to them and no one else.

"We had a grand time the first few days. There was a good wind and the days were long and sunny. Everyone felt fine and looked forward to making their homes in the new country. We planned to sail to Philadelphia.

"But we never reached Philadelphia. For one day we found that the Captain was a brute of a

man and had no intention of taking us to Philadelphia or anywhere. He planned to starve us
and throw all of us overboard then take all the
money and the handsome goods the people had
brought with——"

"What a wicked man!" De Witt cried indignantly. "But Grandfather Clinton must have got
the best of him or you wouldn't be here—nor
would Charles and the rest of my family——"

"You're right," Mr. Green agreed, "but you're
getting ahead of the story, and I don't like to be
interrupted."

"I'm sorry," De Witt apologized. "I won't say
another word, Mr. Green."

"Your grandfather was well-educated. He
studied the situation carefully. He called us all
together one night and told us we must capture
the Captain and put him in irons and take over
the ship. He was sure, he said, that with his
knowledge he could navigate the ship. Back in

Ireland he had been a surveyor and good in mathematics.

"Your grandfather Clinton didn't know that the wicked Captain had told the crew he would share with them what booty he got. The crew was faithful to him and our plan failed.

"That horrible voyage went on for almost five months. We were given less food every day. An epidemic of measles broke out among the children. Your grandparents lost a little girl and a boy. Now they had only one daughter, Catherine, left.

"Once we saw land and one of the crew cried out that it was Virginia. He said he knew the coast line. But the Captain called him a fool and had him beaten.

"At last your grandfather and the other men became so desperate from hunger and thirst that they tried again to make terms with the Captain. The passengers agreed to give the Captain and crew two-thirds of all the money and goods they had. This left very little for themselves.

"The Captain agreed. Food and water were growing scarce for him, too. You know, though, he broke his word to his crew. He kept all that we gave him and never shared a bit of it with them. He never even told them his wicked plan.

"After he landed us on October 4, 1729, another date I'll never forget, he gave them shore leave. Then he collected a new crew and was off the following morning. He was a bad man.

"He landed us on Cape Cod, so we stayed there for a few years. But we didn't like it very much. Your grandfather grew very restless. He wanted to go to New York Province.

"In 1731 some of us came here. We were able to buy this tract of land. It is only six miles from the Hudson River and about sixty miles from New York. It was just what your grandfather and all the rest of us wanted.

46

"We built some rude stone huts and lived in them until we could build better houses. Since I was a lad alone, I lived here with your grandparents and their children. I helped to build this place. That's how Little Britain, New York, was founded.

"Your grandfather became a well-known man in all of New York Province. He was very handsome and respected. People knew that he meant what he said. They trusted him. Life was good to him, too.

"He was proud of his wife and his daughter Catherine, who had survived that terrible voyage. After we reached America, four sons were born to your grandfather and grandmother.

"When England sent over a George Clinton to be the Governor of the Province of New York in 1743, your grandfather and he became friends. They found they were distantly related. George was the youngest son of the sixth Earl of Lincoln and your grandfather was directly descended from the second Earl of Lincoln. You boys have royal blood in you."

De Witt laughed. "We've got Dutch and English and now royal blood. And we're Americans. I like our American blood best of all!"

"Good for you." Mr. Green nodded. "Now it's time you boys started home. Your mother will start worrying about you if you're not there by the time it gets dark."

"That was a wonderful story, sir," De Witt said. "Thank you, Mr. Green."

"Thank you," Charles added. "We wish we could stay longer, but you are right that Mother expects us to come home before dark. We don't want her to worry."

The boys called "Good-by" as they ran across the compound toward their home.

It was almost dark. The time had passed so quickly while they listened to their grandfather's and Mr. Green's exciting adventures that they hadn't realized it had grown so late.

The boys were almost home when De Witt stopped and said, "Hush! I hear something whimpering. Something has been hurt."

They held their breath and listened hard. There it was again—an animal's mournful cry of pain.

"Some animal is caught in a trap!" Charles decided after a minute.

"Let's go help it," De Witt suggested. He started off in the direction from which the moaning sound had come.

"Wait a minute!" Charles cried, running after him. "Suppose it's a fox or a raccoon—they'd bite your hand off if you went near them."

De Witt had already disappeared in the underbrush. Charles hurried after him. If it were a wild animal that might turn on his brother, he could shoot it.

De Witt was kneeling by the trap. A small shaggy black and white dog had caught his front paw in it. De Witt was trying to release the trap. The dog was waiting patiently. He was licking De Witt's busy hands.

"Come and help me, Charles, please!" De Witt cried when he saw his brother. "I can't get this trap off the dog."

In a few minutes they had freed the dog. The paw hung limp and bloody. The dog looked up at the boys with pathetic brown eyes.

"It's poor Judd, the Collinses' dog," De Witt said. "When the Indians burned the Collinses' house, they moved down to New York. They must have left poor old Judd behind. We'll have to carry him home."

"I don't know how people can be so mean as to desert a dog or a cat," Charles said indignantly. "Don't worry, old fellow. We'll take turns carrying you."

Between them they got Judd home. They made a soft bed for him before the fire. Mrs. Clinton soon had the bloody paw bathed and wrapped. De Witt got Judd a bowl of warm milk which the little dog lapped up gratefully.

"We've found a new friend," De Witt said. He patted Judd's shaggy head. Judd licked his hand as if he knew what the boy had said.

An Important Discovery

"COME ON, Judd! Let's take a walk!" De Witt called one bright October morning.

Judd opened one sleepy eye, then the other. He got up from his comfortable bed by the fire. He opened his mouth in a big yawn. He stretched and shook himself. He was ready to follow his young master anywhere. When De Witt opened the door they both sniffed at the cold, stimulating air.

Ever since he and his family had spent the night in the cave which Thunder Cloud had shown them, De Witt had wanted to try to find it again. He wanted to explore it in the daytime.

He wished Charles could go with him. But Charles was the man of the family now since their father and older brother had gone off to war. Charles was busy with farm work and other important things.

Early that morning Charles had announced, "I'm going hunting with some of the men and older boys. We are going to try to track down that old wolf which has been making a lot of trouble for everyone."

"You mean the one that killed the six sheep and two goats in one night?" interrupted De Witt. "It's a bad one."

"Yes, it should be easy to find because its tracks have one footprint shorter than the others," Charles told De Witt. "Remember one time the old wolf had one foot caught in a steel trap and lost some of its toes?"

"I wish I could go, too," De Witt had said.

"You're too young. You couldn't keep up with

us. Besides, you haven't a gun," Charles had replied with firmness.

De Witt had watched his brother join the group of men and older boys. Then he decided to do the next best thing. He would take Judd and search for Thunder Cloud's cave. He and Judd started into the forest.

The forest was no longer an Indian hunting ground. After the terrifying night when so many settlers had their homes burned or had been killed, the remaining men had banded together and driven the Indians many miles away. Now the Clinton boys were no longer forbidden to go into the forest.

De Witt whistled as he tramped along in his good stout boots. The sharp tang of the keen autumn air made his hazel eyes sparkle. It brought the blood to his cheeks. It made him feel as light as a feather, and as if he could walk forever and never tire.

Judd ran ahead. He sniffed the delicious smells, meant only for a dog's keen nose.

They followed the trail for some time. Then De Witt and Judd plunged into the thick underbrush. He thought he had marked the place where they had turned off by a huge oak tree. There were many huge oak trees in the forest, and he hadn't gone far when he realized this was not the right place.

The thick tangle of underbrush and vines caught at his feet. The forest seemed to close around him. He was glad to have Judd for company. Judd stopped suddenly. The black and white hair on his neck and back rose in an angry ruff. He growled deep in his throat.

"Go get it, boy!" De Witt commanded. He thought Judd had flushed a squirrel or a chipmunk. It was a large red fox lying on a bed of dry leaves in an open sunny spot ahead of him. The fox jumped to its feet when Judd rushed at it. It was too quick for the dog. The fox turned like a red flash and disappeared into the forest. Judd went after it.

De Witt shouted, "Come back, Judd!" But the dog was too excited to hear or mind him.

"If I only had a gun!" De Witt thought. "I could shoot it before it could hurt Judd!" He was sure little Judd wouldn't have a chance against the wily red beast.

Walking in the dense forest was hard going. Once a vine sent De Witt sprawling, but he picked himself up and went on. If Judd hadn't kept up an excited yelping, De Witt would not have been able to follow him.

They came to another clearing. Judd started across it. Suddenly with a loud yelp of fear the little dog disappeared into a hole in the ground!

De Witt ran forward. He pushed aside the small bushes that grew thick around. He dropped on his knees beside the hole and peered down into the black depths. The hole was so deep De Witt couldn't see his dog. He heard Judd whimpering far, far below.

De Witt got to his feet. He knew the hole was too deep for him to be able to reach Judd and too deep for the small dog to climb out. What could he do to help Judd? He had to get him out somehow.

He hated to leave Judd alone in the black hole, but De Witt knew he couldn't get him out alone. He must get help.

He knelt down again and called down to Judd. "I'll come back as soon as I can," he promised. "I have to get someone to help me."

Judd seemed to understand. He stopped whining. He gave a quick little reassuring bark. Then he was quiet.

De Witt pushed his way as fast as he could through the wild blackberry vines and the ground pine and pinkster bushes until he reached the trail. Then he ran. Maybe his mother could help him. Maybe Charles had come home.

Then Thunder Cloud stepped out of the bushes ahead of De Witt. "Why run so fast? Something chase you?" he asked.

"Oh, no!" De Witt gasped. He was out of breath from running. "My dog Judd fell into a big hole, and I can't get him out. I was going for help."

"We get dog out of hole," Thunder Cloud said confidently. "Come!"

De Witt hurried ahead. Thunder Cloud followed at his heels.

When they reached the hole, Thunder Cloud knelt beside it. De Witt knelt beside him. "I'm back, Judd!" he called. "I have someone to help. We'll get you out."

Judd gave a small welcoming bark.

Thunder Cloud shook his head. "Not easy," he said. "Hole too deep."

"We've got to try!" De Witt cried. "We can't leave poor Judd down there."

"We try." Thunder Cloud nodded.

Thunder Cloud took out his hunting knife. He reached up and slashed at one of the thick grapevines entangled in a near-by tree. He hacked it free.

He approached De Witt. "Thunder Cloud tie around waist," he explained. "Let you down into hole. You bring dog up."

De Witt backed away. He didn't want to be lowered into that deep blackness. Suppose the Indian lad wasn't strong enough to haul him up again! Suppose the grapevine rope broke! Suppose a number of other things that could happen! De Witt hesitated.

"You afraid!" Thunder Cloud said accusingly.

Judd gave a pathetic little whimper. That caused De Witt to make up his mind. "I am a little scared," he admitted. "That hole is very deep and black, but tie the rope around me. I've got to get Judd."

Thunder Cloud tied the rope quickly and securely. Then he wound part of it around a tree. That would keep it from slipping too fast through his fingers.

Damp and darkness was all around him as De Witt was lowered into the deep hole. The rough rocky walls seemed to close around him. Thunder Cloud was letting the rope out slowly.

By pushing with his feet and hands, De Witt was able to keep the rough surface from bruising him. He thought he would never reach the bottom. At last he landed with a soft bump, and the rope slackened. Judd sprang at him and licked his hand.

De Witt picked Judd up and hugged him. "We'll soon be out of here," he told him. Judd nuzzled in the boy's arms.

De Witt was amazed when he realized that

there was light at the bottom of the hole. He found that he was in a large rock-walled chamber. A set of crude steps had been carved out of one of the rocky walls. Light seemed to come from an opening above them.

Even more startling to De Witt was the discovery that around the walls were piled muskets and rough boxes full of ammunition. There were other wooden chests, too, but they were all closed very tightly.

For a moment De Witt thought, "Do I dare climb the steps and try to get out that way instead of being drawn up through the deep black hole? Where would they lead me? Suppose when I get to the top of the steps that I can't get out. Then what do I do?"

The light was not too bright. Someone might have rolled a stone across the opening. De Witt decided not to go up the steps. He jerked at the rope to let Thunder Cloud know he was ready to be pulled up. He clutched Judd tightly under one arm. De Witt managed to keep from bumping into the rough rocky walls with his feet and his other hand.

De Witt made up his mind not to tell Thunder Cloud about his discovery in the rock-walled chamber down below. Someone might have prepared that place as a hide-out. It might be the Tories. It might be the Indians. It might even be the Americans. He couldn't be sure.

"I'll only tell Mother and Charles," he said to himself. "They'll know what to do."

Judd jumped out of De Witt's arms when they reached the surface at last. He seemed none the worse for his adventure. Thunder Cloud slashed the grapevine from around De Witt's waist.

"Thank you, Thunder Cloud," De Witt said.

The Indian held out his hand. "We friends," he said as he shook De Witt's hand. "Friends help each other."

De Witt whistled for Judd and they started home. Thunder Cloud went with them for a way. Then he slipped into the forest as silently as he had appeared.

De Witt and Judd dashed excitedly on home. De Witt hurried into the kitchen where Mrs. Clinton was cooking their supper. Charles was mending a ripped boot.

"Mother, Mother, Charles, listen! Judd and I have just found something important!" The words came tumbling out as he breathlessly told them his story.

Mrs. Clinton and Charles listened intently while he described his amazing discovery.

"It can't be the Americans who planned to hide there," Mrs. Clinton said when he had finished. "We would have been told. We would have been asked to contribute something——" She went on, "I think we should tell Mr. Green. He has been looking after the settlement since your father went away."

"I think so, too," Charles agreed. He laid down the boot. "Come along, De Witt. We'll go tell him right now."

They raced off to tell their grandfather's old friend of De Witt's discovery.

Mr. Green listened carefully. When De Witt finished his story, Mr. Green clapped him on the back. "You did right not telling anyone but your family about this," he said. "We have known for some time that our Tory neighbors were up to something.

"Time and again when our American soldiers searched their homes for guns and ammunition, we never found any. We knew the Tories had them, and we guessed they had found a hiding place for them.

"Then, too, none of their homes was burned in any of the Indian raids. That meant the Indians fighting under the British had been warned not to bother the Tories' homes.

"I shall call some men together tonight, and we'll get you to show us the way. We'll seize the Tories' weapons and get the better of them."

Mrs. Clinton wasn't pleased when she heard that De Witt had been asked to lead the men to the Tories' hiding place.

"You are far too young," she said. "A six-year-old lad like you should be in bed. Besides, there may be fighting."

66

"He has to go," Charles pointed out. "Otherwise the men won't know where to find the hole. I'm going with him. I'll look after him."

"All right," Mrs. Clinton consented, "he may go if you will bring him home as soon as he shows the men where the supplies are hidden."

It was after eleven o'clock when Mr. Green knocked on the door and asked for De Witt. A party of grim-faced, silent men followed the boys into the forest. They carried ropes and lanterns.

When they reached the hole, De Witt explained how Thunder Cloud had lowered him into it. The slimmest man in the crowd was chosen to go down first. He was to carry a lantern and climb the rough steps De Witt had described. If the entrance was not covered over, he was to get out that way and come and tell the others about what he found.

De Witt watched the man being lowered by ropes into the big black hole. He knew exactly how he must feel as he was lowered into the rock chamber below.

Soon the rope slackened. Everyone knew the man had reached the bottom.

"Come on, De Witt," Charles said firmly. "We have to go home now. I promised Mother."

"But I don't want to go home until we know whether there is another entrance to the hole," De Witt protested.

"Yes, De Witt, you must go on home with Charles now," Mr. Green insisted. "You have been a real patriot tonight. Your father and brother will be proud to learn of the share you are taking in the war with the British. You have led us well. Now you must remember a good soldier knows when to fight and when to rest. Go back home to keep our promise to your mother."

De Witt trudged home. He soon fell asleep with his hand on Judd's rough coat.

The Messages

De Witt was out in the back lot. He was chopping wood. It seemed sometimes as if the fireplace could never be satisfied. The late sun caught the bright blade of his ax as he swung it back and forth. He was proud that now he was seven he was allowed to use the ax.

De Witt stopped chopping for he heard a sound in the distance. The *rat-a-tat-tat* of a horse's hoofs came closer. They stopped before the house. De Witt dropped his ax. He ran to see who had arrived.

De Witt hoped it might be Father or Alexander home for a few days' visit and rest. He was disappointed to see that it was a postrider. He handed Mrs. Clinton a letter.

"Won't you rest a while and have something to eat?" De Witt heard his mother ask. He was glad she had, for the man's face was tanned by wind and sun and his leather boots were covered with mud and dust. He looked as if a rest would be good for him.

The rider shook his head. "Thank you," he said, "but I haven't time today. I must get this mail on its way." He jumped on his horse and touched his hat. Then he galloped away.

Mrs. Clinton called her sons together. "A letter from your father!" she exclaimed. Her eyes were shining. She held the letter as if it were a very precious thing.

She took her seat on the high settle before the fire. The boys gathered around her.

"My Dear Ones": the letter began. "How are you all? I miss you terribly and hope times have

70

not been too difficult for you. I know you boys will look out for your mother. Take care of her. On my fortieth birthday, which you know fell on August 9, 1776, I was appointed a Brigadier-General by the Continental Congress. Wasn't that a fine birthday gift?"

The letter was long and full of news and the boys listened closely to every word. Finally he wrote, "And now for the best news of all. I am quite sure it has not as yet reached Little Britain. So you shall be among the first to know and you shall tell our friends and neighbors so they can rejoice with you. A Declaration of Independence has been written by our good friend, Thomas Jefferson. It was adopted by the Continental Congress. On July 4, 1776, a date I want my sons to remember with pride all the rest of their lives, it was read from the Courthouse steps to the people of Philadelphia. The Liberty Bell, as they have named the great bell that hangs in the belfry, rang out the message of freedom. It was a proud moment for all Americans who have been praying and fighting for our freedom——"

Young De Witt sprang to his feet. His handsome face was aglow. "Hurrah!" he shouted. "Hurrah for the Declaration of Independence! Hurrah for Mr. Thomas Jefferson who wrote it! Hurrah for the Liberty Bell! Hurrah for Father and Alexander and all the Americans who are fighting for our freedom!"

Charles and little George jumped to their feet and shouted, too. Little George wasn't sure what the excitement was all about, but he wanted to be in on the fun.

Mrs. Clinton smiled. "I see you will never forget July 4, 1776," she said. "How pleased your father would be if he could see you now!"

A few months later another rider stopped at the Clintons' house. He didn't bring a letter.

But he brought news. He accepted Mrs. Clinton's invitation to rest for a moment and have something to eat and drink.

He had come a long way and he had a still longer way to go. He told his news while he ate and drank. The Clintons all gathered around him to hear what he had to say.

"The British have entered New York City," he began. "They have burned part of the town. General Washington and his troops were forced to retreat to Harlem Heights. There they were forced to retreat again when Fort Washington was taken by the British.

"The Americans marched to White Plains. They gallantly defended that small town, but the British were too strong for them. They were slowly pushed across the Hudson River to New Jersey. The British soldiers and the Indians followed them. They were finally chased all the way to Pennsylvania——"

74

Mrs. Clinton wrung her hands. "Is there no way to stop them?" she cried.

"Don't fear, ma'am! We'll stop them!" the man said. He stuck out his chin and looked so brave and strong that De Witt was sure that he would try to stop the British Army alone.

"Our brother Alexander and Uncle George are with General Washington's army!" Charles exclaimed. "They must have been in all that fighting!"

The boys admired their Uncle George Clinton very much. He was their father's younger brother. He had been chosen in 1775 to be one of New York's delegates to the Continental Congress. They knew from their father's last letter that on July 2, 1776, Uncle George had cast his vote for independence. Immediately after that he too had been made a Brigadier-General by the Continental Congress. He went off to join General Washington's army.

The rider continued with his message: "I have been sent to warn the people along the Hudson River that since Westchester and New Jersey have fallen into British hands, their soldiers and Indians are planning to march to Albany.

"The British hope to cut New York Province in half. The people of Westchester and the lower Hudson valley have already suffered from their ruthlessness. The British have given the Indians free hand.

"The red men swoop down wherever they please. Both the Indians and British rob and burn the settlers' houses. They take some of them captive. They hold these poor people for a high ransom. The enemy will be coming up the river very soon."

"They'll not pass West Point!" Mrs. Clinton declared. "My husband and his brother George helped in making the chain that has been placed across the river. No British ship can pass it!"

The man shook his head. "Let us hope so, ma'am!" he said. He left soon after.

"Perhaps we should go to stay with Mr. Green in Grandfather Clinton's house," Mrs. Clinton considered.

She looked around the pleasant room and sighed. "How I hate to leave my things," she went on sadly. "So many hold such happy memories——"

"Why can't we stay right here?" Charles demanded. "If De Witt will help me, we can build strong shutters for the windows. We can put other locks on the doors. We would be as safe here as anywhere. Besides, Mother, you and I have guns. We could hold off any raiding party that comes here."

"If I had a gun I could help, too," De Witt said wistfully.

"You are right," his mother agreed. "You are old enough now to have a gun of your own. We will go to Mr. Green tomorrow. We'll ask him to give you one of Grandfather Clinton's. I am sure he will be glad to do it."

De Witt thought his heart would burst with pride. Now he would have his own gun, one that had belonged to his grandfather. What more could any boy ask!

Thanksgiving

ALL THAT spring and summer De Witt Clinton worked hard and learned how to handle his gun very well. He was very proud of it and he kept it clean and shining. He kept it near him all day. It stood at the head of his trundle bed at night.

He always took his gun with him when he went into the forest. He brought his mother plenty of squirrels and wild pigeons to make into pies. One day he brought home a wild turkey.

"Mother," he said when he placed it on the kitchen table, "can we celebrate Thanksgiving this year? It's the day after tomorrow. Here's the turkey for a part of our dinner."

"We shall!" his mother cried enthusiastically. "We've been sitting around nearly a year waiting for those old British and Indians to come up through the valley or by the river. It's time we had a party and a little fun!"

How the house buzzed with the preparations! How hard everyone worked! There were currants to pick and boil and make into jelly. There were onions and potatoes and cider and apples to be brought up from the wooden bins in the cellar. There was bread to be baked. The turkey had to be stuffed. There were pumpkin and apple pies to be made.

"We're going to have a real party," Mrs. Clinton, her cheeks like red roses from bending over the fire, declared. "We'll ask Mr. Green and the Reverend John Moffat and his family."

"Will the Reverend bring Lucie?" De Witt asked. He liked Lucie. She was a year younger than he. They often played together.

"Of course he'll bring Lucie. I shall ask him to bring all his family," Mrs. Clinton declared.

"The Moffats have so many children that sometimes they leave a couple of them at home. They think people may not like to have so many in their house at once," De Witt explained.

"You shall carry my invitation. Be sure to tell them we want all their family to come. We especially want to see the new baby!" Mrs. Clinton said.

De Witt was very proud as he marched off to deliver his mother's invitations to the Thanksgiving party. He carried his gun. He wanted to show Mr. Green how well he had learned to use it in the last few months.

De Witt wanted to impress young Lucie. She didn't know he had a gun. He hoped she would think a boy his age was pretty smart to own a gun of his own—especially one that had belonged to his grandfather.

Everyone accepted the invitation gladly. Mrs. Moffat was particularly pleased that Mrs. Clinton had included all of her family.

"I do not like to leave any of them at home," she told De Witt. "But some folks think twelve young ones are an awful lot to ask to a party."

"They all must come," De Witt said. And he added, "Especially Lucie."

Mrs. Moffat smiled. "She'll be there," she told him.

Thanksgiving morning was gray. A thick layer of snow covered the cold earth. Angry-looking clouds scudded across the sky. There was a promise of more snow in the bitter cold air.

"Do you suppose all of them really will come to the party?" De Witt asked his mother anxiously. He knelt on the window seat and shook his dark curly head at the threatening weather.

"Of course they will," Mrs. Clinton assured him for the tenth time. "A little snow never kept anyone from a party and a chance to have a little fun. There haven't been enough good times lately. Now stop moping. Run down to the cellar to bring me some more apples."

De Witt brought up the apples for his mother. Then he went back to the window. He stayed there until he saw the huge sleigh carrying the large Moffat family coming across the clearing.

He hopped down from the window seat and shouted, "They're coming!" He raced to the door to open it.

The Moffat family hurried into the firelighted, warm room.

Mrs. Clinton hurried to meet them, too. There were twelve Moffat children. They ranged from fifteen-year-old Matilda to tiny Harold, the three-month-old baby.

Mrs. Clinton had Charles bring down George's cradle from the attic. Charles placed it in her room. Soon young Harold, wrapped snugly in his own blankets, was fast asleep in the cradle.

The other children soon got over their shyness. Then the house rang with their young voices and happy laughter.

Mr. Green arrived at last. He carried an odd-shaped parcel. When he opened the package two dozen carved and highly polished wooden plates fell on the table.

"I thought these would save you washing a lot of dirty dishes after the party," he explained. "Had one of the boys who likes to whittle make them up for me. Just burn them when we're through with them."

Mrs. Clinton thought the plates were wonderful. "But I hate to burn them," she said, "they're so pretty."

"If you like them there will be plenty more where these came from," Mr. Green told her.

The good friends and neighbors crowded

around the long table. What a feast it was! Soon there was nothing left of the turkey but bare bones. The potatoes, onions, and other delicious things disappeared like magic. The apple and pumpkin pies were there one minute and gone the minute after!

"We should have more parties like this," Mr. Green told Mr. Moffat later. The two men were seated before the blazing fire, relaxing and smoking their pipes after dinner.

"It keeps up our spirits and helps us forget the war for a while." Mr. Moffat nodded his agreement. He was a clergyman and a man of peace. To him this war, although he disliked it very much, seemed a necessity.

Mrs. Moffat and the two oldest Moffat girls were helping Mrs. Clinton clean up. The younger children were playing an exciting game of blindman's buff.

Nobody heard the horses stop outside the

85

house. Nobody heard the door open. Quietly two tall men wrapped in Army capes stepped into the room.

Mrs. Clinton was bending over the fire. She was burning the last of the wooden plates Mr. Green had brought her.

Mrs. Clinton's face turned white when she saw the two men. She held out her arms and ran across the room. She threw herself into the arms of the taller, older man.

"Oh, James," she cried. "You've come home at last! And George, too," she added, holding out her hand to greet her brother-in-law.

What a Thanksgiving present that was! Charles, De Witt, and little George rushed to their father and their Uncle George. The men gathered around them.

After a while Mr. Moffat said quietly, "I think it is time we went home and left this family to enjoy their happiness alone."

He and his wife collected their twelve children. Mr. Green decided to ride along with them. At last all that could be heard was the merry jingle of the sleighbells in the icy air.

"What a Thanksgiving this has been!" Mrs. Clinton sighed. She and her husband were alone at last. George Clinton had left soon after Mr. Green and the Moffats. He was anxious to get home to his own family who didn't live too far away. The boys were in bed. A peace had settled over the house. Mrs. Clinton, with her soldier husband under the same roof, felt secure once again.

A Birthday
Present

DE WITT's father's stay with his family was very
short. It seemed to De Witt and his brothers that
he had just arrived when he was off again. But
how everyone enjoyed those few days!

Mr. Clinton took the boys fishing in the Hudson River, which was six miles away. He was
immensely proud of the way the boys had
learned to handle their guns. He helped Charles
and De Witt make heavy shutters for all the
windows of the house.

James Clinton agreed with his wife Mary that
she and the children would be safe in their own
house. Grandfather Charles Clinton had given

89

James and Mary this house for a wedding present. Mrs. Clinton did not want to leave it. Since they decided to stay, Mr. Clinton kept repeatedly warning them always to be on the alert.

The morning he was leaving he called De Witt to him. "I have made arrangements with the Reverend John Moffat to tutor you," he told De Witt. "He was kind enough to agree to do it. He knows a lad of eight needs to learn more than nature can teach him."

De Witt was delighted. "Thank you, Father," he said. "I want to learn more about everything. I like Mr. Moffat." Only to himself did he say that now he would see Lucie every day.

"I know you have always been interested in curious rocks and stones and trees and flowers and birds and fishes," his father went on.

"I know, too, you enjoy reading. Your mother has told me that you have finished reading our slim collection of books. Mr. Moffat will be able to teach you more about your rocks and things, and he has a fine library."

Every day after his chores were done De Witt went to Mr. Moffat's home for three hours of lessons. He enjoyed the quiet room where Mr. Moffat studied the Bible and wrote his Sunday sermons. No one ever disturbed them there.

De Witt was a good scholar. He learned quickly. Mr. Moffat was pleased with him. He enjoyed teaching a boy who was bright and paid attention. He gave De Witt the beginning of a sound classical education.

The threat of the British and Indian raids hung like a black cloud over the country. Nobody dared venture anywhere without a gun. De Witt tried to be as good a soldier at home as his father, brother, and uncle were in battle.

Time passed quickly. Soon it was March 2, 1778. De Witt woke up that morning to find his mother and brothers gathered around his bed.

"Happy birthday!" they cried in unison.

His mother kissed him nine times, then gave him an extra tenth kiss "to grow on." Charles and George slapped him on the back nine times and gave him a particularly hard whack, "for luck," they told him.

When the fun was over, Mrs. Clinton said, "Get dressed and come to see your presents."

De Witt scrambled into his clothes. He ran into the family room. There were gifts from everyone spread out on the big oak table.

His mother had made him three handsome new shirts. Charles had sent to New York for a book about botany. Mr. Moffat had recommended it.

Young George had made him a wooden cup. He had carved the initials D. C. on it. The letters were a little crooked, but De Witt thought the cup was fine.

Mr. Moffat gave him a Bible. Lucie had

knitted him a long red scarf. Mr. Green had sent a new hunting knife.

"Here is something your father sent you," Mrs. Clinton said after everything had been looked at and admired. She opened the door of a cupboard and brought out a small uniform.

The uniform was an exact duplicate of the ones worn by the American soldiers. The dark blue coat, buff-colored trousers, black boots, and cocked hat had been made to fit De Witt perfectly.

"Your father had it made for your birthday," Mrs. Clinton explained. "I sent him your measurements and he had his tailor make it up. Go put it on and let us see how you look in it."

De Witt looked very handsome dressed in the uniform. The cocked hat sat proudly on his dark curly head. He was tall for his nine years and he looked even taller as he held himself erect. He marched up and down before his family. He

pretended his mother was General Washington. He saluted her smartly.

"The uniform is a great success!" Mrs. Clinton declared happily.

"May I go and show it to Mr. Green and Mr. and Mrs. Moffat?" De Witt asked after breakfast was over.

"And Lucie," Charles said slyly. He liked to tease De Witt about the pretty little Moffat girl.

"And Lucie!" De Witt said good-naturedly. "May I, Mother?"

"Of course, dear," Mrs. Clinton replied. "This is your day. You may do whatever you like."

"I like a birthday better than Christmas," De Witt said. "I like having 'my day.' Christmas is nice, too, but it doesn't really belong to any special person."

"Except the little Christ Child," Mrs. Clinton reminded him. "Now run along and show yourself in your new uniform to all your friends."

De Witt walked slowly. A boy didn't run and jump and whistle when he was wearing a uniform. Judd went along, too. Since Judd wasn't wearing anything he had to respect, he rushed ahead and enjoyed himself as only a dog could be expected to do.

Mr. Green came to attention and saluted De Witt smartly. He had been in on the secret. He thought De Witt looked very handsome. Mr. Green wished De Witt's father could see him. "Turn around slowly, boy," he said. "Let me see the whole thing."

De Witt did as he was asked.

"That's the best-looking and the best-fitting uniform I've ever seen!" Mr. Green declared. "It's mighty becoming to you."

"I liked my new hunting knife you sent me very much, too. Thank you for remembering my birthday, Mr. Green," De Witt told him. Then he described his other presents.

"Your father would be very proud if he were here to see you," Mr. Green said. He stood on the porch and watched the boy march across the compound. Mr. Green was proud of his young friend, too.

De Witt marched even straighter when he approached the Moffats' home. He hoped Lucie might be looking out of a window.

Lucie was spinning when one of her younger brothers opened the door for De Witt. Because she was too small to reach the tall wheel, she was standing on a wooden stool. The white thread she was spinning was straight and even. Any older woman could have been proud to have spun such thread.

Lucie clapped her small hands when she saw De Witt. "Oh, you look wonderful!" she cried. He almost burst with pride. He felt now his day was complete. Lucie had seen and admired him in his new uniform.

The whole Moffat family gathered around. Mrs. Moffat gave him a bun, hot from the oven. She put plenty of butter on it. It tasted delicious. How kind they were! Their kindness did much to make his birthday a happy one.

He wore his uniform all the rest of the day. He sighed when he took it off at bedtime and hung it up in the cupboard in his room. "I wish I could always wear it," he told his mother, who had come in to kiss him good night.

"You may if you like," Mrs. Clinton told him. "You grow so fast these days I am afraid it may soon be too small for you. So get as much wear from it as you can."

De Witt was delighted. "Thank you, Mother," he said.

Of course, De Witt didn't wear his handsome uniform while he was chopping wood, feeding the pigs and chickens, and doing the other couple of dozen chores boys had to do while their fathers were away. He always wore it when he went to Mr. Moffat's for his daily lessons. If he had no more chores when he came home, he kept it on until bedtime. He took very good care of it.

Mrs. Clinton was very proud of her young son who so highly respected the uniform of his country. "He is a fine lad," she thought.

The Wolf Hunt

Mrs. CLINTON snapped shut the lid of a small horsehair-covered trunk and turned to De Witt. "You may put that in the wagon," she said.

De Witt lifted the trunk to his shoulder and carried it out to the springless wagon. The wagon was already piled high with the Clintons' clothing and household goods.

Mary Clinton and her children were taking their most treasured things with them to New Windsor. They were going to visit some of their Clinton cousins who lived there.

"We'll never get to New Windsor if we don't start soon," Charles called to De Witt.

De Witt seemed puzzled.

"I can't make up my mind whether to take my collection of odd rocks or my book about botany," De Witt answered. "Mr. Moffat gave it to me as a farewell present. I haven't had a chance to read it yet."

"Take the book," Charles advised. "It won't take up so much room. If you haven't read it yet, you may get a chance to do so after we get settled in New Windsor."

"Maybe there will be some new kinds of trees and bushes in New Windsor," De Witt said. "I could check them in the book."

The Clinton relatives had invited Mary Clinton and her boys to visit them and stay as long as they liked.

Mrs. Clinton had accepted the invitation gladly. "A change will be good for all of us," she had said in her reply.

"How long are we going to stay?" young

George asked. He didn't like to leave the new duck a neighbor had given him. Mr. Green was going to take care of it for him. But George had looked forward to seeing the little yellow, fluffy fellow grow up.

"That depends upon when the British and Indians come near the town," Mrs. Clinton replied. "Come on, children, let's get started now. It's a long trip."

They soon made themselves as comfortable in the wagon as possible and were on their way.

"The British got through to Kingston," Charles reminded her as they bounced along over the bumpy road. "I think——"

"Mr. Moffat told me they set fire to every house in the village," De Witt broke in. "He was very sorry they burned Mr. Addison's Academy, too. Mr. Moffat said it was a fine school. He said he had hoped I might go there someday when the war is over."

"All the people in the villages on both sides of the river keep packed and waiting for news," Charles said. "I guess it will be the same way in New Windsor."

"Then why can't we turn around and go home?" little George asked. He was still thinking of his duck.

"We were nice and comfortable at home," De Witt added as he put an arm around Judd. He was very grateful that Judd was being allowed to go with them.

"Your father said in his last letter that he would feel we were safer if we stayed with his people for a while," Mrs. Clinton said.

De Witt looked at his mother in her plain gray homespun dress. She wore a small black bonnet. There was a rose tucked under the brim.

"How pretty she is," he thought, "and how brave. It must be very hard on her to leave the home which she loves so much."

He was right. It was hard for Mary Clinton. She was the kind of woman who thought of her home as a fortress which she must protect.

After a tiring journey, they reached New Windsor at four o'clock in the afternoon. The Clinton family came out to greet them. Everyone helped carry in the baggage.

De Witt had a time sorting out the different members of the family. There were the father and the mother. They were easy to distinguish. There were three girls all older than he or Charles. Then there was a boy just about Charles's age and another, named Robert, who was just right for De Witt. The youngest child was a year younger than George.

All the children were somewhat shy at first. After a good hot supper the shyness disappeared like magic, and they became friends.

De Witt shared a room with Robert. When they were tucked in bed Robert said, "Father is organizing a wolf hunt tomorrow. He said we could go along if we promised not to get in the way of the men."

"I've never been on a wolf hunt!" De Witt said. He was terribly excited.

"You'll like it," Robert said. "This one is to catch a very sly and mean old wolf. She has been coming back every year with her whelps."

De Witt interrupted. "Did they kill your sheep and goats and pigs?"

"Yes," replied Robert. "She and her whelps are a great nuisance, and they cost us settlers a lot of money. The whelps get killed off every year, but the old wolf is too smart to be caught. The men vow they'll get her this year."

The next morning dawned bright and clear. Barking dogs awakened De Witt and Robert. The boys bounded out of bed and ran to the nearest bedroom window.

A group of men with guns and hounds had

collected in the front yard. The men looked grim-faced and ready to attack their common enemy, the wolf.

"De Witt, hurry up and get dressed!" Robert shouted excitedly.

De Witt scrambled into his clothes. He gulped down his breakfast. He grabbed his gun and he was ready.

Judd rushed around barking like mad. Robert looked down at the small black and white shaggy dog. "You had better leave Judd here," he said. "He might get hurt."

De Witt looked down at the eager little dog which was wriggling all over in happy anticipation. He knew Robert was right. Judd was too small to take along, but he knew he wasn't going to enjoy himself half as much without Judd. He called Judd to him and explained that he had to stay here at Robert's house.

Judd seemed to understand. He put his tail

between his legs and retired to the front porch. He sat there with his sad brown eyes fixed on his young master. Judd hoped that De Witt might give in at the last minute and let him go along to hunt for the wolf.

The air smelled of wood fires and of burning leaves. There was a brisk wind.

De Witt was glad to have on a warm coonskin cap. Charles had given the coonskin cap to him when their mother had made Charles one of squirrel skins.

De Witt recalled how he and Charles had brought the squirrels to their mother one day a long time ago. He recalled, too, how Mr. Green had told them of the adventures he and their grandparents had had on their way to America from Ireland.

The coonskin cap felt good pulled down around his ears on that chilly morning.

The hounds soon picked up the scent of the

wolf. The hounds followed her trail. They bayed loudly as they rushed ahead.

De Witt kept well up in front. He was used to pushing through heavy growths of underbrush. His legs were long and strong.

As De Witt hurried along, he kept his eyes open for a new specimen of a bush or a tree which he could tell Mr. Moffat about when he got back to Little Britain. His interest in botany had developed a great deal since he had been studying with Mr. Moffat.

Suddenly everything was quiet. It was quite a relief. The hounds had stopped baying. The men had stopped shouting.

"They have driven the wolf into her den!" Robert explained excitedly. His voice sounded odd on the quiet air.

Mr. Brundridge called to his dogs. "Go and get the wolf!" he commanded.

The three big dogs dashed forward. A narrow

opening led to the wolf's den which was hidden under a steep cliff.

What noises came out of the darkness! Snarling and barking and yelps of pain. In a few minutes the dogs crept out. They had all been badly hurt by the wolf's sharp claws and teeth. They slunk to their master. They refused to return when Mr. Brundridge commanded them to do so. They were frightened.

"Somebody has got to go in and shoot the wolf," Robert's father decided.

One by one men stepped forward and volunteered to go in, but they were all too large to get through the narrow opening in the side of the cliff. Each man turned away unhappily.

"What are we going to do?" Mr. Brundridge asked. "While we are standing here talking, the beast may slip out some back way we don't know about and escape again."

De Witt stepped forward. He was the youngest boy in the party. "I think I could get through that passage, sir," he told Mr. Brundridge.

The other men and boys stared at him.

"We couldn't let you go!" Mr. Brundridge said bluntly. "You're only a young boy. It would be too dangerous."

"You want that wolf shot, don't you, sir?" De Witt went on.

"We certainly do," Mr. Brundridge declared heartily. "But how could a mere lad like you help us shoot him?"

"Wild animals are afraid of fire," De Witt explained. "If I can have a couple of strips of birch bark, I could make a torch——"

"Birch bark!" Mr. Brundridge interrupted. "Why birch bark?"

"Because it will make a good strong light for me to see by in the dark den," De Witt answered confidently.

"Listen to the lad!" one of the group who had

been listening sneered. "Birch bark, indeed! Who ever told you that birch bark would make the best light?"

"I read about it in a book. Mr. Moffat and I made some experiments. Birch bark burned the best and made the clearest light," De Witt replied politely.

"Who's Mr. Moffat?" the sneering man went on. "I've never heard of him."

"He is a Presbyterian clergyman who lives near us in Little Britain. He is my teacher," De Witt told the man.

"Why not let the boy try?" someone in the crowd cried.

"Yes, let him try," the sneering man agreed. He didn't care what happened to De Witt. He sort of hoped the wolf would give him a good scare—maybe claw him a little.

De Witt threw down his cap. He took off his overcoat and his undercoat.

Mr. Brundridge tied a rope around his waist. "You give a pull on that when you want to come back. We'll have you out in a jiffy," he told the boy reassuringly.

A man lighted the birch-bark torch for De Witt. He handed it to him, and De Witt crouched down and entered the narrow opening to the den. He moved cautiously. His blood tingled. His heart pounded. He knew what danger lay ahead. How dark it was! The torch threw a small circle of light, and he crept on into the wolf's den.

Suddenly in the darkness ahead De Witt spied the flaming eyeballs of the wolf. She was frightened by the sight of De Witt's burning torch. She gnashed her teeth. She growled and snarled at the boy.

De Witt knew there was no time to lose. He pulled the rope. He wanted to get out of there as fast as possible.

When Mr. Brundridge and the men heard the
wolf growling and snarling, they thought De
Witt was in grave danger.

"Give a hand here!" Mr. Brundridge shouted.
Half a dozen eager hands seized the rope. They
hauled De Witt out fast—so fast that his shirt

came over his head, and his hands and knees were skinned.

"You're the bravest boy we ever knew," Mr. Brundridge exclaimed. "Are you badly hurt? Did she try to jump you?"

"Not this time——"

"I wouldn't have gone into that den if they had paid me!" Robert said. "Weren't you badly scared?" the boy added.

"I was kind of scared," De Witt admitted. "But I'm going in again. I'll shoot the wolf next time. I'm sure I can."

"We're not going to let you!" Mr. Brundridge cried. "You've had enough."

"Please, sir, let me go down again. I started out to kill that wolf and I mean to finish the job," De Witt declared.

"I don't want you to get hurt. We had better just hope the wolf dies down there," suggested Mr. Brundridge.

114

"No, I am going right back down there and shoot that wolf now," insisted De Witt.

"All right. We will let you go again, but let me fasten another rope around your arm. In case you shoot the wolf, fasten this second rope to her. We will haul you both up." Mr. Brundridge finally agreed.

De Witt crept into the dark passage again. He carried his birch-bark torch in one hand and his gun in the other.

Soon he saw the wolf. She looked fierce and terrible. She howled in rage. She rolled her eyes and snapped her big white teeth. She lowered her head between her front paws. She crouched ready to spring at De Witt.

De Witt dropped his torch and raised his gun. He aimed at the angry wolf and pulled the trigger. The blast of the gun blew out the torch. It stunned De Witt, too, for a moment.

The blackness was terrifying. He wasn't sure

he had killed the wolf. If she had just been wounded she would be frantic with pain. She might spring on him at any moment.

He jerked hard at the rope. He didn't care how fast they pulled him out this time! Just so he could get away from the dark and the smell of the gunpowder and see the daylight again.

"We heard your gun go off," Mr. Brundridge said when De Witt was safely out and on his feet again. "Did you kill the beast?"

"I don't know," De Witt admitted. "The torch went out, and I couldn't see." He blinked at the daylight a couple of times. Then he refilled his gun quickly and skillfully.

"Will someone please light another torch for me?" De Witt asked. "I'm going down again. I want to make sure I killed her. If I didn't, I will this time."

"You're the stubbornest boy I've ever met!" Mr. Brundridge thundered. "With a will like

116

that you should go a long way when you're a man! But I'm afraid for you now."

De Witt's uncle grinned. "You can't stop a Clinton, let alone a De Witt, once he has made up his mind!" he said. "Let the lad go."

De Witt crept through the narrow opening for the third time. He carried his gun and torch again. The wolf was lying on her side. She seemed quiet. He kept his gun cocked as he crept closer and closer. She did not move. She was dead.

He jerked at the rope three times. That was the signal that would tell them he had killed her. Then he tied the extra rope around the great beast's neck. He jerked his own rope, and out he went! They hauled up the dead wolf next.

The men crowded around De Witt and shook his hand. They slapped him on the back and praised his bravery. The sneering man shook his hand, too. He apologized.

De Witt laughed. "There is a lot between the covers of a book besides the pages," De Witt told him.

The man grinned sheepishly. "I'll remember that," he said.

De Witt thought to himself that he would long remember his first wolf hunt when he and his family had returned to their own home.

A Visit with Thunder Cloud

De Witt ran all the way home from Moffats' house. He was a hot and tired thirteen-year-old who came bursting into his home to tell his wonderful news. His dark hair stood on end. His eyes were sparkling. His cheeks were red from excitement and from the run.

"I've been accepted at Mr. Addison's school in Kingston!" he shouted. "Mr. Moffat just told me. He's very pleased. You know he had always hoped I could go there someday."

Mr. Addison's Academy was a very famous institution. It had been burned down with other buildings by the British and Indians when their

Army had occupied Kingston. When the British left, the Americans had begun to rebuild their town. Mr. Addison's school had been one of the first buildings to be erected.

"I am pleased and proud of you," Mrs. Clinton said. She began to plan. "You must have two new suits and shirts and stockings. Oh, dear, how shall I ever get you ready!"

De Witt burst out laughing. "I don't go until September, and this is only June," he said.

Thunder Cloud stuck his head around the door, a welcome visitor now. Mrs. Clinton, as well as the boys, was always glad to see him.

"Thunder Cloud want to take De Witt to visit his people," he announced. "You let him come?"

De Witt's mother knew that Thunder Cloud's people were friendly to the Americans. She knew her son would want to go. So she didn't hesitate a moment. "Of course he may go," she told the Indian boy.

De Witt rode proudly beside Thunder Cloud through the forest. It didn't take long to reach the Indian village. Thunder Cloud had told his people about De Witt. They all wanted to see the white boy. Some of the children climbed to the roofs of the long houses for a better view.

"Come and see where you will live," Thunder Cloud said.

De Witt followed him. The Indians had set aside two end compartments in one of the long houses for the boys. De Witt lowered his head when he entered the low-roofed place.

The long house was about eighty feet long and seventeen feet wide. There was a six-foot-wide passage down the center. The compartments on either side of the passage were raised about a foot from the ground.

De Witt observed that the compartments were divided by bark walls and each section was about seven feet long. There was a place overhead where their belongings could be kept. There were several fireplaces in the long passage. Over each one a hole had been cut into the roof in order that the smoke could go out.

Thunder Cloud watched De Witt with amusement. "You think we be wet when it rains and water comes through holes." He laughed. "This is what we do——" He picked up a long pole and pushed a piece of birch bark over the hole. "See! No rain. We no get wet." He pushed the birch bark aside again.

"That's a smart idea!" De Witt said admiringly to his friend.

"You wait," the Indian boy went on. "Thunder Cloud get food."

De Witt sat down on the edge of the platform which, later, would be covered with woven reeds and made into his bed. Thunder Cloud returned with two bowls of hominy.

Thunder Cloud seated himself on the floor.

De Witt slipped down beside him. He was surprised at how hungry he was. The hot hominy with maple sugar on it tasted very good.

When they finished, Thunder Cloud took the bowls and put them on the shelf over De Witt's bed. De Witt didn't like that. He would rather have washed his bowl.

The boys stepped out into the sunshine. De Witt looked around with interest. He had never visited an Indian village before.

"What's that?" he asked. He pointed to a long shedlike building. Its walls and roof were made of bark. It had one door which faced the south.

"My people store wood in there in winter. They sit in there in summer. Sometimes children play in it when it rains," the Indian lad explained to his friend.

De Witt saw oak, hickory, white walnut, wild plum, and apple trees. Bushes had been planted thick around the apple trees.

Thunder Cloud grinned and explained. "Bushes keep small children from eating fruit before it is good for them."

"Before it is ripe." De Witt nodded. "That's a good idea."

They came to the sugar maple grove. "We tap trees in early spring. Sap good—taste sweet," Thunder Cloud said.

"I know. I liked it on the hominy," De Witt agreed. "It was very sweet."

"You like play lacrosse?" Thunder Cloud asked suddenly.

"I don't know, Thunder Cloud. I've never played it," De Witt answered.

"They play it now. We go watch." Thunder Cloud led the way to an open spot where a crowd of Indians was gathered. Thunder Cloud found good places for De Witt and himself to watch the game.

De Witt had heard of the game lacrosse, but

he had never seen it played. He was very much interested. He saw that two poles about six feet apart were fixed in the ground. Two more poles were about six hundred yards away.

Two teams took their places. One Indian stood exactly between the goal posts. He threw the ball high in the air. The teams rushed forward.

De Witt saw that each player carried a stick about three feet long. There was a sort of racquet made of deer thongs fastened to one end of the stick. It looked like a large hand.

When the players rushed forward, they tried to catch the ball in this racquet. One Indian did. He then threw it at a great distance. The game had started.

It was a fast game. It was rough, too. De Witt saw an Indian boy have his wrist broken when a racquet came down across it. Another fell and was trampled on by the frantic players.

De Witt was pretty sure now he didn't want

to play lacrosse—not the way the Indians played it, anyway.

At last the team who wore red feathers stuck in their headbands won.

Thunder Cloud got to his feet. "Come," he said. "Thunder Cloud teach you other game. You not get hurt." He saw that De Witt hadn't enjoyed the lacrosse game very much.

He led De Witt to a shady spot under a tall maple tree.

"Wait here," he said. "Thunder Cloud not be away long."

De Witt dropped down on the soft moss under the tree. Thunder Cloud returned shortly. He had run to the long house. He brought back one of the bowls that had held the hominy. He put the bowl down between them.

Thunder Cloud produced eight little four-sided bones from the beaded pouch he wore around his waist. The bones were about the size of plum pits. Two of their sides were painted white. The other two were painted black.

"See bones," Thunder Cloud explained. "Take turns. Throw up in the air. Count bones that go in bowl with black side up."

The Indian threw the bones up in the air over the bowl. Three fell into it. Two of the three had the white sides showing.

"You play now," he told De Witt. "See which one get forty blacks first."

De Witt threw the bones. Six of the eight fell into the bowl. All six had their black side up.

"You play good!" Thunder Cloud praised him. De Witt was the first to make a score of forty black. He won the game.

Other Indians had gathered around. A tall Indian man stepped forward. "Me play winner," he announced. De Witt looked up at him in surprise. A man wanted to play with him! Why, he was only a boy!

De Witt won again. He was having what his father would have called "beginner's luck." One after another the Indians took turns to try to win, but De Witt didn't seem to be able to lose.

The Indians became more and more excited. They began to shout and scream every time De Witt tossed the bones in the air. They spoke to the bones as if they were human beings. The Indians called on the spirits to stop De Witt's good luck.

The shouting bothered De Witt. He didn't like it. He was glad when at last he lost a game and could stop playing. The Indians played against one another now. They shouted and screamed even louder.

Thunder Cloud and De Witt grew tired of watching them after a while. De Witt was glad when it was bedtime. He stretched out on the woven mats of rushes. He pulled the light deerskin cover over him. He fell sound asleep.

128

He was awakened by a shout. He opened his eyes and gasped. A weird-looking figure was bending over him.

De Witt saw the strange figure wore a mask made of bark. The nose was five inches long. A grinning mouth with long white teeth and glistening eyes with circles of yellow paint and outer circles of white paint around them made the mask hideous and frightening. Long black locks of buffalo hair hung down on either side of it.

The figure carried a long staff in one hand and in the other a gourd. This gourd had small stones in it. The gourd rattled when it was rubbed up and down the staff. Suddenly the frightening figure brayed like a donkey.

De Witt pushed himself up in bed. He was alarmed by this strange person.

"Lie down!" Thunder Cloud called from the apartment across the passage. "Brown Bull will not hurt you. He is to make you laugh."

De Witt lay back as Thunder Cloud had told him. He couldn't see anything to laugh about in the weird figure which was now prancing before him. Sometimes Brown Bull pulled the buffalo hair across the hideous mask. Then, bending over De Witt, Brown Bull would give a sort of animal bray and thrust the hair back so that De Witt had a closer view of the ugly face.

Suddenly Thunder Cloud leaped out of bed. Thunder Cloud struck the floor three sharp blows with his foot. The hobgoblin figure stopped its prancing. Brown Bull, too, struck the floor three times. Then the wild figure jumped out the door and disappeared. The ugly animal noises died away on the night air.

De Witt had a hard time getting to sleep after that. He was honored that Thunder Cloud had asked him to visit the Indian village, but he was glad to be going home the next day.

The rest of the summer passed quickly. At

130

last the time for De Witt to leave for Mr. Addison's school arrived.

He awakened early the day he had to go to Kingston. He lay in bed and looked at all the familiar things he would so soon be leaving. How long would it be before he saw them again? Would they ever seem the same to him?

He looked at the chest of drawers his father had made for him one Christmas. He looked at the wooden shelves Charles had knocked together for him. He kept his collection of odd rocks on them. All these possessions meant home to him. Suddenly he didn't want to go away to school.

"Get up, De Witt," Charles cried from the other bed. "The stagecoach will be stopping for you in an hour!" He hopped out of bed. De Witt jumped up, too.

His new blue suit felt stiff and scratchy after his comfortable old summer clothes. The collar of his new white shirt seemed to want to choke him. The new shoes were tight and squeaked when he walked.

"You look grand!" Mrs. Clinton exclaimed when he went down to breakfast. He did not feel grand. He felt uncomfortable and self-conscious in his new outfit.

The stagecoach stopped at the door. Mrs. Clinton kissed De Witt good-by. Charles handed up the small wooden chest which held De Witt's clothes. George clung tightly to Judd, who was trying to jump on the stagecoach with his master.

"Want to sit up by me?" Mr. Scott, the red-faced driver, asked. He felt sorry for the handsome little boy in his new blue suit. He hoped it would take De Witt's mind from his leave-taking if the boy sat up beside him.

"Thank you, sir," De Witt said, as he scrambled up on the high seat. "I would like that!"

Away they went! Mr. Scott flourished his whip over the backs of the four horses. De Witt looked back until his family and his home were only specks in the distance.

"Like to drive for a bit?" kind Mr. Scott asked after a while. He knew the way to Kingston from end to end. Ahead lay a piece of flat, clear road.

De Witt's eyes sparkled. "I've never driven four horses," he admitted. "I'd like to very much, but I'm not sure that I can."

"It's easy," Mr. Scott said, "once you get the hang of it. Let me show you."

De Witt learned quickly. He was so proud and delighted to be driving the handsome coach and the four brown horses that he forgot his homesickness. Mr. Scott let him drive to the outskirts of the town of Kingston. Then Mr. Scott took the reins again.

"Good luck, lad!" he told De Witt when they drew up before the school. He handed down the wooden chest. As he drove away, he saluted De Witt smartly. De Witt watched until the coach turned a corner. Then he knocked on the green-painted door of the school.

Mr. Addison, a kind-faced, gentle-spoken man, opened the door himself.

"I am glad to meet you, De Witt Clinton," he said. He shook De Witt's hand and led him into the hallway. An older boy came forward and helped De Witt with his wooden chest.

"Please take over, Stephen," Mr. Addison told the boy. "See that De Witt Clinton is made to feel at home."

From that moment on De Witt did feel at home. He had always been a good and eager student. Mr. Addison was an excellent teacher. He made the lessons interesting and easy to learn. De Witt was very happy at the school. He was glad he had come.

A Reward

De Witt sat at the long oak table. There was a book open before him. De Witt was reading an English history book Mr. Moffat had lent him. De Witt made notes as he read. He liked to read history books. He thought they were as interesting as any storybook and, besides, everything in them had happened to real people. He was home from Mr. Addison's Academy at Kingston for the summer holidays.

The war with the British had ended at last. De Witt's father was having a well-earned visit with his family. He was not out of the Army yet. There were a great many things to be straightened out. General George Washington had not dismissed his men. He was giving almost all of them long leaves of absence.

De Witt heard his father come into the family room. He looked up expectantly.

Mr. Clinton chose a comfortable chair by the fireplace. He drew out of his pocket the short corncob pipe he smoked when he was working. The long-stemmed white clay pipe he smoked when the Clintons had guests hung in its special place above the low wooden bookcase. De Witt knew his father was settling down for a leisurely smoke and rest.

De Witt knew this usually meant he was in a storytelling mood. De Witt hoped he was now. De Witt never tired of hearing his father tell of the British Army's surrender at Yorktown, Virginia. His father never seemed to tire of telling about it. He had been with General Washington all through the seige of Yorktown.

De Witt got up and went over and drew up a stool beside his father's chair. "Will you tell me more about that day in Yorktown?" he asked. "Didn't you receive the colors of the defeated enemy?" He knew the story by heart, but he liked to hear it over and over again.

His father looked down at him and smiled very gently. "Yes," he said. "I was privileged to receive the colors."

"Please tell about the storm that came to help the Americans win!" De Witt begged. He liked this part of the story very much.

"It was the worst storm I have ever seen," his father went on gravely. "The lightning flashed, the thunder roared, and the rain pelted down. The British General, Lord Cornwallis, was desperate. Cornwallis was hemmed in between the French bombardment from the sea and the Americans by land. His one way of escape was to cross the river with his men that night. Once in Maryland, he hoped to join forces with another English general who was marching down from New York."

"But they couldn't cross the river because of the bad storm!" De Witt exclaimed with satisfaction and certainty.

"No one could have crossed that night," his father said. "The boats would have been swamped a few feet from shore."

"And the next day the Americans and French started storming Yorktown again!" De Witt cried excitedly. "And finally General Lord Cornwallis told his drummer boy to play the tune which was a signal for a parley, which meant he was ready to talk surrender terms."

"It seems to me you know as much about that day as I do," his father said good-naturedly.

"Oh, no!" De Witt protested. "But I remember every word you have told me. And I never tire of hearing you tell it over again."

"Well, the guns stopped thundering. Suddenly it seemed strangely silent. I tell you we missed the noise. Then across the battlefield we heard the music of the Scottish bagpipes. They played a tune to make your feet dance and your heart beat fast.

"Later a French band struck up a gay march. It was hard for us to believe that after all the years of fighting the British at last had surrendered. We had won the war with the British.

"The men who were chosen to represent General Washington and General Lord Cornwallis met at a near-by farmhouse. They wrangled a long time over the details of the surrender. Finally at noon they agreed on the final terms.

"The conditions of surrender were written down and brought to General Washington. I was with him, and I watched him while he read the document. He read it twice. Then he took his pen and wrote, 'Down in the trenches before

Yorktown in Virginia, October 19, 1781.' Then he signed 'G. Washington' and handed it back to the soldier who had delivered it."

"October 19, 1781," De Witt repeated. "That's another date to remember, like July 4, 1776, when the Declaration of Independence was signed in Philadelphia."

"You are right." His father nodded. "Those are two very important dates in American history."

De Witt was sorry when his mother called his father away.

De Witt had a lot to consider. He wondered if it were not going to be hard for the Americans to become used to their newly won freedom and independence. They had been fighting for it for the past seven years.

De Witt remembered how many nights he and his family had gone to bed not at all sure they would be alive in the morning. At any time a raid could have swept down upon them.

Now they could go to sleep without fear and they could go about their daily tasks without carrying a gun.

One cold November day an elegant coach stopped before the door. De Witt peeped out the window. "Who can that be?" he wondered. "I have never seen such a handsome coach." When the well-dressed man stepped out of it he shouted, "It's Uncle George!" and rushed out to greet his kind uncle.

Uncle George Clinton had become the Governor of New York Province. That important position had not changed him. To De Witt and all the Clinton young people he was still their jolly uncle. He was always a favorite relative with all the Clinton family. He was a very handsome man. He was tall and distinguished-looking.

He laughed down at De Witt and clapped him on the shoulder. "You grow like a weed!" he exclaimed. "Last time I saw you, you came to my shoulder. Now you are almost as tall as I am, my boy!"

De Witt grinned. "I'm fourteen, sir," he said.

"That's quite an age!" the Governor said. There was a twinkle in his eye. "I have come to pick up your father to drive to New York with me. We have both been invited to take part in the ceremonies when the British evacuate."

How De Witt wished that he could go with his father and uncle. How exciting it was going to be! He wished he were older. Then he could have gone by himself.

The Governor was to spend the night. He and De Witt's father planned on an early start.

De Witt slipped out to the stable after supper. He walked around the elegant coach. He rubbed his hand along its highly polished sides.

He opened a door and climbed in and sat down on the softly padded, tan satin seat. How comfortable it was! How wonderful it would be for him to be traveling to New York City in it tomorrow! De Witt sighed unhappily.

Everyone retired early. Suddenly De Witt awakened with a start. He sat up in bed. He sniffed. He smelled smoke! He hopped out of bed. Since Charles was away visiting a friend, De Witt was in the room alone. He ran to the door and looked out. He saw a red glow outlining the doorway of the family room!

"Help, Father, Uncle George, the house is on fire!" De Witt shouted as he dashed toward the kitchen. He quickly snatched the bucket of water that he knew always stood there.

He ran back to the family room. When he threw open the door, he saw a fairly large hole burning near the fireplace. Evidently a spark from the fireplace had started the fire.

De Witt immediately dumped his bucket of water on the fire. The fire sizzled, but it did not go out. He flew out to the pump in the yard.

144

When he got back with the second pail of water, his father and uncle had stamped out the fire with their great heavy boots. "Pour it on for good luck," his father said. "There may be a spark or two left."

Nobody slept much the rest of that night. At breakfast the next morning Governor George Clinton said, "None of us might be enjoying this delicious food if De Witt had not smelled the smoke last night and used his head. I think he should be rewarded. Is there anything you would like especially, my boy?"

"Oh, yes, sir!" De Witt cried. "I would like to go to New York with you and Father."

"Do you think you could spare him, Mary?" Governor Clinton asked.

"Of course! He shall go if that is what he wants! Run and pack your things, De Witt."

De Witt flew away to pack. He didn't want to keep the men waiting.

The Evacuation

THE TRIP to New York in the elegant coach was more wonderful than De Witt had dreamed. People stepped out of their doorways to salute his uncle, Governor Clinton. Men stopped working in the fields to bow respectfully.

Children stopped their play and stared with round, awed eyes as the coach rolled by. Other children ran out to present small, damp-stemmed bouquets. Governor Clinton always knew the exact things to do and say.

De Witt saw that people liked and respected his uncle. He was proud to be his nephew.

The coach drew up at last before Governor

Clinton's house in New York City. De Witt was glad to see his cousins, and they were delighted to see him. He was tired from the long journey. But he was too excited to sleep.

He lay on his back and listened to the unfamiliar noises of the city. He heard the cries of the sedan-chair carriers as they hurried through the streets. He heard the *clop, clop* of horses' hoofs on the cobblestones. Then there came the reassuring voice of the watchman as he swung his lantern and called, "Nine o'clock and all is well!"

He thought he had just closed his eyes when his cousin woke him the next morning. De Witt was soon up, dressed, and eating his breakfast. The very air tingled with excitement. Everyone was busy getting ready for the big day ahead.

The Governor's wife came into the dining room. A tall, shy boy followed her. "This is John Pintard," Mrs. Clinton told her sons and De Witt. "He is spending the day with us."

148

De Witt liked John Pintard the minute he met him. They at once became good friends. De Witt felt as if he had known him all his life.

There were four saddled horses waiting in the street for the boys. They mounted them and rode to the Dove Tavern. It was some miles from the city. The parade was to start from there.

"Look!" John Pintard told De Witt as they neared the tavern. He pointed to a man who was painting a sign by the side of the road.

The sign had once held seven stars, but now the man was busily adding six more. The new white paint glistened in the sunlight.

"Those thirteen stars stand for our thirteen states, just as the thirteen red and white stripes in our flag represent our states," John went on.

The boys were very excited to be in the midst of such an event as the evacuation of the last of the British Army from New York. Bells were ringing. People were running and shouting.

The boys left their horses at Dove Tavern and hurried to find good places to watch the beginning of the celebration. Suddenly a wave of cheering broke out. People shouted and clapped their hands. Governor Clinton's boys, De Witt Clinton, and John Pintard shouted and clapped louder than anyone.

General George Washington rode past on his beautiful white horse. Governor George Clinton rode beside him. Behind them came De Witt's father and General Henry Knox and his staff. De Witt's heart swelled with pride as his father saw him and gave him a special salute.

Then, marching proudly, came the victorious American Army. Some of the men wore handsome new uniforms. Some were in their tattered old uniforms. Some of them were still in rags.

They all held their heads high and stepped along to the well-known tune of "Yankee Doodle" played so well by the drum and fife corps of their regiments. That tune had led them into many a battle. Now it was a song of triumph. John Pintard started to sing the words:

> "Father and I went down to camp,
>   Along with Captain Gooding,
> And there we see the men and boys
>   As thick as hasty pudding!
> Yankee Doodle keep it up,
>   Yankee Doodle, dandy,
> Mind the music and the step
>   And with the girls be handy."

De Witt laughed. He had never heard those words before. He liked them, and he liked the snappy rhythm of the tune.

Behind the marching soldiers another troop of horses came along. They were ridden by loyal citizens who had done their share to help the American Army win the war.

When the parade had passed, the boys got their horses from the Dove Tavern. They fell in behind the parade and followed it until they reached the top of the Bouerie Road. There they dismounted. Two of Governor Clinton's grooms were waiting to take care of the horses.

The boys ran to join the crowd of men, women, and children who were following the winding Bouerie Road to the city. Along the way they passed many war-torn homes of both English and Dutch. There were no more Union Jacks, the British flag, waving. The American flag was hung over many a simple cottage door. At last they reached Queen Anne Street.

"I don't like the name of this street," De Witt said. He wanted a good American name for it.

"It is going to be renamed Pearl Street," John Pintard told him.

At last the procession reached the Fort at the end of Manhattan Island. To everyone's surprise, a Union Jack still fluttered above the Fort. The crowd screamed and shouted. They wanted their own flag to fly there, but the British had greased the flagpole. They had cut the rope by which their flag could have been hauled down.

A man wearing spiked shoes stepped forward. He saluted General Washington and said, "I think I can climb that pole, sir."

The General nodded his approval and the man stepped up to the pole. In a short time he had climbed the pole, let the Union Jack down, and hauled the Stars and Stripes into place.

How the people cheered! They lifted the man to their shoulders and carried him over to General Washington and Governor Clinton. Both of them shook his hand and congratulated him.

"Look at all those ships in the bay," De Witt exclaimed. The British were loading one as he spoke. De Witt watched sad-faced families of refugees moving up the narrow gangplank. He felt sorry for them. He knew they were leaving forever their homes and the friends they had made in America.

"They are being taken to Nova Scotia," John told De Witt.

What an exciting day it had been! The twenty-fifth of November, 1783, was another date he would always remember.

Two days later John Pintard came around to see De Witt. "Are you game for an adventure?" he whispered when the Governor's sons were out of hearing distance.

De Witt nodded eagerly.

"General George Washington is going to say good-by to his officers tonight at Fraunces' Tavern," John told him. "I know how to get up to the Long Room where they are going to meet. We could, perhaps, see the whole thing."

"I am sure my father and my uncle would not like for me to go," De Witt replied.

"I will admit we mustn't tell your Clinton cousins," John Pintard said. "We might get caught. We wouldn't want to get them into

154

trouble because their father is the Governor of the state. Just you and I should try it."

"All right," agreed De Witt, "I'll go."

It was well after dark when De Witt and John crept up the back stairs at Fraunces' Tavern. John had made friends with a kitchen boy, and he showed them the way. There was a door at the top of the stairs. There was a cupboard near by. Brooms and mops were kept in it.

"You can hide in there if you hear anyone coming," the kitchen boy told them. "There are four peepholes in the door of the Long Room," he went on. "The waiters use them when a meal is being served there. Then they can tell when it is time to change the plates and bring on another course."

De Witt and John took their places. De Witt's heart beat fast with excitement. Suppose his father and his uncle found out! They would punish him, he knew.

The boys took their places by the door. The peepholes gave them an excellent view of the Long Room. The officers were beginning to arrive. De Witt saw his father and his Uncle George in their dress uniforms. He recognized General Knox and several other officers. He had met some of them when they had come to see his father in Little Britain.

Finally General Washington arrived. De Witt thought he was one of the handsomest men he had ever seen. How tall he was! How well he carried himself! He threw off his long blue military cape and gave it and his black cocked hat to an attendant. His white wig gleamed in the fire and candlelight. He spoke in the voice of a man who is used to giving orders and having them obeyed. He was a born leader of men.

De Witt knew this was another memory he would never forget. These serious-faced men had lived and fought together for many long

years. There was a mingling of happiness and sadness in this their last meeting.

At last they lined up to clasp the hand of their leader in farewell. De Witt saw tears in their eyes, but he knew that these strong men, who had fought so bravely and so well, were not ashamed of the tears.

De Witt heard General Washington say to Governor Clinton, "I am going back to Mount Vernon. I am looking forward to renewing my life there."

"I shall retire to the more peaceful duties and to the task of reconstruction of our state," Governor Clinton said.

"I shall be at home," De Witt's father said. "I shall teach my children other lessons than those of caution and independence."

The time for the final farewell came at last. General Washington looked at the officers who had been his trusted friends for so many years.

He spoke with feeling. "With a heart full of love and gratitude I now take my leave of you, most devoutly wishing that your latter days may be prosperous and happy as your former ones have been glorious and honorable."

The next day De Witt was so excited that he told his father what he and John had seen.

His father looked at him sternly. "It is unworthy of you, my son, to have become a deceiver and an eavesdropper. I shall have to punish you severely."

De Witt took his punishment without a whimper. He knew he deserved it. He was sorry he had done wrong. But he was glad that he had heard a great general bid farewell to his officers in the Long Room of Fraunces' Tavern.

Columbia College

"Mr. Addison says you are ready for college," Mr. Clinton told De Witt, one day in early May.

"Yes, sir," De Witt replied. "I suppose I'll go to Princeton, won't I?" All the Clintons who had gone to college had gone there.

"No, son," Mr. Clinton said. "Since King's College has been remodeled and people have donated money for its support and new collection of books, I have decided you shall go there."

De Witt was delighted. The newly named Columbia College, which had once been King's College, was in New York City. That meant he would be near his uncle's family.

He took the entrance examinations later in May and passed them successfully.

De Witt was now fifteen. Father and son prepared for the trip to New York to continue De Witt's education. Both welcomed the opportunity to share future plans on their long ride through the country.

How New York had changed since they had last been there! The burned houses had been replaced with handsome new ones. The roads had been repaired.

De Witt and his father spent the night at the Governor's house. The next day De Witt moved in with a Mr. and Mrs. Gano. He liked his plain room which contained plenty of shelves for his books and the odd rocks and shells and dried plants he was still collecting.

After his father left for home, De Witt decided to take a walk. He felt a bit homesick.

He could picture his family sitting around the

long oak table in the family room. The candles would be lighted. The fire would be leaping on the wide stone hearth. His shaggy little black and white dog would be curled up before it. The cat would be dozing on her cushion.

Polly would be hemming a fine piece of linen. She was the oldest of De Witt's three little sisters. George would be carving a set of wooden spoons. Mother would be knitting, the firelight dancing on her pretty hair.

His father would still be traveling back to them along the dark roads. How glad they would be to see him!

A crowd of men rounded a corner ahead of him. The men were hustling someone along. De Witt ran to see what was happening. When he drew close enough he saw it was an Indian in the center of the crowd. Suddenly De Witt recognized him. It was Thunder Cloud!

He pushed his way through the crowd of men.

He grabbed the Indian's arm. "Thunder Cloud!" he cried. "How did you get here? What are you doing in New York?"

"Thunder Cloud come to see you," the Indian lad began. The men broke in, and wouldn't let him finish.

"Is your name De Witt Clinton?" one asked. His voice was cross.

"Yes, sir," De Witt replied.

"You know this Indian?" the man went on.

"Yes. He is one of my best friends," De Witt exclaimed. "What has he done that you are treating him this way?"

"He went to Mr. and Mrs. Gano's house where you have a room. He pushed his way in and demanded to see you. They were afraid. They asked him to go, but he wouldn't leave. They called for help, and we are now taking him to jail where he belongs."

"Thunder Cloud only want to see you," the

Indian explained. "People you stay with grow afraid because I do not want to leave. They call these men. I do not understand."

"He is my friend," De Witt repeated. "Please let him go. I will take him home and explain to Mr. and Mrs. Gano. I will make them understand that he meant them no harm."

The man who had asked all the questions protested. "He goes to jail," he said. He looked around the crowd. Nobody seemed to agree with him. No one made a move.

"De Witt Clinton is the nephew of Governor George Clinton," one man said. "We'd better let the Indian go. We don't want to get into any trouble."

The crowd began to disappear. Finally the cross man went away, too.

De Witt thought he had never been so happy to see anyone as he was to see Thunder Cloud. The boys walked to Mr. Gano's house. De Witt

164

introduced Thunder Cloud to Mr. and Mrs. Gano and explained that he was a friend.

He asked their permission for Thunder Cloud to spend the night with him. They agreed, but they looked frightened. They didn't like the idea of an Indian sleeping under their roof. They brought up enough supper for the hungry boys. Soon Thunder Cloud's good-natured smile won them over.

"You may have my bed," De Witt told the Indian boy when it was time to retire.

Thunder Cloud shook his head. "Me sleep here," he said. "No like soft bed." He spread his blanket on the floor and was soon fast asleep.

"This is my first day at college," De Witt told Thunder Cloud the next morning. "I can't take you with me. What will you do all day while I am away?"

Thunder Cloud drew himself up proudly. "Do not worry, kind boy," he said with dignity.

"I tell you I come to see you. That is part truth. But I come to New York to be in-ter-pre-ter."

"You mean you are going to tell the white people what your people are saying—and the Indians what the white people are saying?" De Witt cried. He thought it was a fine idea. He would see a lot of Thunder Cloud if his friend stayed in New York.

Thunder Cloud nodded. "Your Uncle George and your kind father get work for me——"

"That is fine!" De Witt declared. "You must stay with me until you find a place of your own."

"Thunder Cloud no like to sleep in houses," the Indian said. "Like it better in open. I find someplace outside city to stay."

"Suit yourself," De Witt said. "But come here whenever you would like to do so. You will always be welcome."

He grabbed his hat and his books and ran down the stairs. The air was fresh and balmy.

The former King's College, now Columbia, was not completed as yet. DeWitt had been told that the first classes would be held in a temporary room in the City Hall, on Wall Street.

The teachers were waiting for their pupils. The Reverend John Gross taught geography. The Reverend Benjamin Moore taught rhetoric. Mr. John Kemp had the task of teaching mathematics.

De Witt liked all his teachers from the start.

He liked his classmates, too. One boy, named Abraham Hunn, he liked particularly. They walked home from school together that evening. Another boy, Francis Sylvester, walked part of the way with them. De Witt thought college life was going to be very pleasant.

The days passed quickly. He wasn't homesick any longer. His brother Alexander was in New York, acting as Governor Clinton's secretary. Charles had come down from Little Britain. He was studying to become a surveyor. The three boys enjoyed being together. They went to parties that their aunt, Governor Clinton's wife, gave. They had a gay time.

One day in late September, De Witt, Abraham Hunn, and Francis Sylvester decided to go for a ride. Abraham's father had a stable full of horses. De Witt and Francis were able to borrow two lively ones.

They rode up toward Greenwich Village. More and more people were spending the summers in the little town, which was not too far from the border of the city. Almost all of the houses were closed now.

The boys enjoyed riding through the autumn woods. They raced their horses under the clear blue sky. They dismounted by the side of a brook and rested on the soft moss and leaves along its banks.

"Let's take the trail along the Hudson," De Witt suggested when they were ready to go home. The others agreed. It was a narrow, rocky trail and not many people used it.

Abraham led the way. Francis and De Witt followed. The blue water of the Hudson River sparkled in the sunlight.

Suddenly Abraham's horse slipped on a loose rock. Horse and rider plunged over the embankment and disappeared.

De Witt and Sylvester sprang off their horses. They scrambled down the bank. Abraham was clinging to an overhanging branch of a tree. The horse, which had been caught in a swift current, was being carried quickly down the Hudson River.

As the boys pulled Abraham to safety, they heard a loud shout behind them. A slim figure rushed past them. It was Thunder Cloud! He dived into the water and started swimming strongly after the frightened horse.

"The Indian will drown!" Abraham cried.

"He can't fight that current if he does get to the horse. He'll never make it."

De Witt watched Thunder Cloud battle his way down the river. He clenched his hands tightly. He was afraid that what Abraham had said was true.

The boys watched for five tense minutes. It seemed more like ten hours. They saw Thunder Cloud, now just a small speck in the distance, reach the horse.

They watched the Indian boy jerk the bridle and turn the horse toward shore. Still swimming strongly, he made for the bank at a point farther down the trail.

The boys climbed up to where they had left their horses. Abraham got up behind De Witt. Then they rode down to where Thunder Cloud and the horse were trying to land.

They got there just in time to help the Indian lad and the horse come ashore. The horse was

still wild-eyed from fright. Abraham soon had him quieted down.

Thunder Cloud lay down under a pine tree to rest. The battle with the current had been almost too much for him.

The three boys crowded around him. They made a great fuss over what he had done. "Champion is my father's favorite horse," Abraham told him. "I don't know what I would have done if he had been drowned."

"How did you ever get here in time to save Champion?" De Witt asked Thunder Cloud.

The Indian lad grinned. "Remember me told you Thunder Cloud not like to sleep in houses?" he said. "So I built a bark shelter up by trail. Me see horse's danger. So I save him."

"You certainly got there in the nick of time," De Witt told him.

That was the last time the boys took the dangerous trail along the Hudson River.

The years slipped by fast. De Witt was a good student, and the professors enjoyed teaching the clear-eyed, intelligent boy. He was the first youth to graduate from Columbia College. On Tuesday, April 11, 1786, the Continental Congress and both Houses of the Legislature came to take part in the ceremony. The men marched with the graduates from College Hall to St. Paul's Church for the ceremony.

As the young graduates took their places at the front of the church, De Witt saw his Uncle George, his aunt, his mother, his father, his brothers and sisters seated in the front pews.

Professor Cochrane called the speakers in their proper order. "Mr. De Witt Clinton will give an oration in Latin."

De Witt felt his knees knocking together. It was the first time he had spoken in public. When he finished, he made a polite little speech in the same language to the Members of Congress and the Legislature, to the regents and professors, and to the audience. He was glad when it was over and he took his place with the other graduates. He received his Bachelor of Arts degree.

The Clintons gathered at Governor George's home that evening. De Witt's future plans must be heard and discussed. Would De Witt like to be a surveyor like Grandfather Charles? Would he like to be a farmer and soldier like his father? Would he like to be a statesman like his Uncle George? Would he like to be a doctor like his Uncle Alexander and Uncle Charles? Just what did he want to do?

"I should like to become a lawyer," De Witt told the family.

"Then you shall!" his mother and father said in unison. They knew he had given the matter of his future serious thought.

"I am a little disappointed," his uncle, the Governor, said. "I confess I had hoped that politics might interest you, and I could help you in some way."

"I am sorry, sir," De Witt said, "but I would like to study law."

"I know just the man to tutor you," his father said. "I shall take you to see my friend Mr. Samuel Jones tomorrow."

Mr. Jones was glad to receive De Witt as a clerk in his law office. De Witt learned both English common law and the laws of real estate. In this way, he continued his schooling under the personal supervision of a great lawyer.

A Great Dream

A GREAT CROWD had gathered around Governor Clinton's house on Pearl Street in New York City. "We want De Witt Clinton!" they shouted at the top of their voices.

"Go out, my boy, and take a bow," Uncle George said. He was very pleased with De Witt, who had just received word that he had been elected a New York State senator.

How the people cheered! De Witt smiled and waved to them.

The Clintons sat down to an excellent meal. As the dessert was being served, a servant came to announce that a Mr. Platt wished to see

De Witt. De Witt hurried out to greet his friend and colleague in the Senate. He led Mr. Platt into the library and closed the door.

"How is our favorite project coming along?" he asked. One of De Witt's cherished dreams was that someday there would be a canal connecting Lake Erie with the Hudson at Albany.

Barges loaded with food and goods from the western part of the state of New York could then be taken to New York City all the way by water. The cost of transporting these things by water would cost about half as much as by land.

"You have read Mr. Jesse Hawley's letters concerning the building of the canal," Mr. Platt answered. "Many people feel that it can't be done. Even Thomas Jefferson has said it is madness to think of digging a ditch four hundred and forty miles long through the wilderness."

De Witt laughed. "We will certainly get nowhere if we let these people influence us," he said. "My grandfather, Uncle George, Father, and even President Washington have seen the desirability of expanding to the west."

Mr. Platt smiled wryly. "You and I seem to be the only ones in the Legislature who feel that way, too," he said. "You must talk to the senators and the assemblymen."

"I'll do my best," De Witt assured him.

De Witt kept his word. He made a study of the whole matter. He went to see surveyors, engineers, and merchants. He listened closely to all they told him.

When De Witt was sure he could not possibly be wrong, he began to talk to the Legislature. The senators and the assemblymen began to come around to his way of thinking. They formed a Canal Commission, which met on July 2, 1810. De Witt was a member. Another member was Simeon De Witt, a cousin of De Witt.

The senior member of the Commission was

Gouverneur Morris, a statesman and a scholar. A well-known Dutch landowner, Stephen Van Rensselaer, who was a backer of every public improvement, was appointed. The other members, William North, Thomas Eddy, and Peter B. Porter, all held to the one idea that the canal must be built.

The Commission started from Albany, New York, up the Mohawk in two river boats, to map out the course for the canal. Sometimes, when

the work was done, they fished over the side of the boat or shot fowl along the way.

De Witt had not enjoyed himself so much since he was a young boy. He liked landing on a convenient bank and cooking the fish or birds. He showed the men how Thunder Cloud had taught him to bake potatoes and roast corn in the ashes of the fire.

It was a hazardous trip, too. There were rapids which few boats had ever passed through.

All the men of the Canal Commission made notes of the lay of the land along the Mohawk River. Their journey took them all the way from Albany to Buffalo.

When they got back home, some of the men were discouraged. They didn't see how a canal could be built through the miles of wilderness they had just traveled. De Witt Clinton believed that such a canal was practical, and that someday his dream would be a reality.

The Years Pass

THE YEARS rushed by. De Witt was happily married. He had fine sons and daughters. His life was full and brimming over.

"I am prouder of you than I ever have been," his wife told him on the day he had been appointed mayor of the city of New York. She rode beside him in the open carriage. They bowed and waved to the cheering crowds which lined the streets on either side.

De Witt asked that the procession might pass by the Governor's house on Pearl Street. Members of his family who had gathered there at the windows waved and smiled. Little did anyone

182

realize that De Witt would hold the office of mayor for twelve years, interrupted only by his work in the New York senate and other political positions.

One evening De Witt rushed home. He caught his pretty wife in his arms and whirled her around the room until she was breathless.

"I have wonderful news!" he cried. "I have been nominated to become President of the United States!"

His wife caught her breath. "You have what?" she demanded.

He repeated the news. But it didn't turn out to be happy news after all. De Witt was defeated by Mr. James Madison, who was elected President of the United States.

De Witt didn't let the defeat send his spirits down. He went on in politics. He became Governor of New York State as his Uncle George had been before him. People knew that he was a man they could trust. They knew he always kept his word. They loved and admired him. He was elected Governor three times.

Busy as he was he never forgot his favorite dream, which was the building of the Erie Canal, and he never stopped fighting for it. He had never forgotten the wastelands he had seen when the first Commission had traveled over the proposed route of the canal.

He had never forgotten the small clusters of houses in Buffalo, Rochester, and Utica. He wanted to bring prosperity to these small communities and to other settlements.

These places were growing slowly because of the high cost of having their farming products transported by land to the larger cities like Albany and New York. The waters of the canal would carry things much cheaper. Erie Canal would open the trading possibilities of western New York State.

"It is a dream that will take years to come true," De Witt's brother Charles told him. "If it ever does," he added, for he, like many other people, didn't think the canal could ever be anything but a dream.

De Witt stuck out his chin. He was sure the canal would be finished someday. He had begun the canal when he was first elected Governor in 1817. Then he had broken the ground for its beginning in Rome, New York. He well remembered how thrilled he had been as he had tossed aside the first spadeful of rich earth and had listened to the people cheer.

"Wait and see!" De Witt told everyone. "Someday you will be traveling on a comfortably outfitted barge all the way from Buffalo to New York. You will be sending your products all the way by water at about half or less the cost you now have to pay to send them by land."

"We'll wait and see," they all answered. Some

had faith like De Witt. Some didn't believe it and thought how they would make fun of him when his plan did not come true.

His friends nicknamed him "The Father of the Erie Canal." His enemies called the canal "Clinton's Ditch."

De Witt never lost his faith.

The Erie Canal

On the twenty-sixth of October, 1825, De Witt rose early. He pulled aside the window curtains. The sun poured in on him. "That's a good omen," he said to himself, and hurried to get dressed.

He and his family entered the dining room. A waiter rushed forward. He bowed low. "This way, Your Excellency!" he said.

De Witt laughed when he sat down at the table. "It seems I have a new title," he said to his wife. He grinned widely.

"You should be used to titles by this time." She smiled. She began to check them off. "First

Assemblyman, then Senator, then Mayor of New York City, next Lieutenant Governor, and now for the third time you are Governor of New York State." She beamed with pride.

De Witt smiled. "The titles I like best are father and husband," he said.

By ten o'clock a great crowd had gathered at the dock in Buffalo. They shouted when he stepped across the gangplank and climbed to the deck of the "Seneca Chief."

"Some people call Governor Clinton the Father of the Canal," a woman said.

"He *should* be called the Father of the Canal because he has been interested in it for a long time," her husband added.

"Hurrah for Governor Clinton!" everyone was shouting.

De Witt was very happy. He took his place on the deck of the barge. His wife stood beside him. His children and his illustrious friends gathered

around him. He waved and bowed to the cheering crowds of people.

Four beautiful white horses were harnessed to the barge. Bells began to ring. A band struck up "Yankee Doodle." Flags flew in the stiff October breeze. The people shouted louder than ever as the beautifully decorated barge began to move slowly away from the dock.

Boom! Boom! Boom! went a cannon.

Cannons had been placed every few miles apart at different points along the way. Each cannon would be fired. The sound of the last cannon would be the signal that the "Seneca Chief" had begun the trip through the canal.

It would take only eighty-one minutes for the news to reach New York that the Erie Canal was open at last. The "Seneca Chief" would be ten days carrying De Witt and his companions to New York City.

The "Seneca Chief" moved slowly down the Erie Canal from Buffalo to Albany with its precious cargo of a keg of water from Lake Erie.

When the "Seneca Chief" reached Albany, the dock was crowded with distinguished men. Mayor Philip Hone headed a committee from New York City. What a greeting De Witt received! The people cheered just as loudly as they had in Buffalo.

The "Seneca Chief" was now ready to enter the Hudson River. It could no longer be drawn by the four horses. A flagship named the "Chancellor Livingston" was waiting to tow her down the Hudson River.

Many other gaily decorated steamboats followed them on the historic trip to the Atlantic Ocean. The cheering crowds along the banks of the river, the flower-decorated barge, and the boats draped in bright-colored streamers created a scene of great gaiety on the otherwise gloomy November day.

It took two days to reach New York. What a welcome awaited them there! As the "Seneca Chief" neared the shore, De Witt bowed and waved. The people seemed to be wild with happiness. They shouted forcefully.

De Witt stepped from the barge to the deck of the "Chancellor Livingston", and the gentlemen who had accompanied him on the long trip from Buffalo followed him. De Witt's wife and children and the ladies all went aboard the flower-covered barge "Lady Clinton."

De Witt Clinton solemnly poured the waters of Lake Erie from the symbolic keg with its gilded hoops into the Atlantic Ocean. Tremendous cheers rose from the throngs of people.

"They call this the wedding of the waters," Mrs. Clinton said. "But I think of it as the end of a wonderful dream."

De Witt Clinton was justly proud to have his dream come true at last. What he had started out to do had been finished and was successful. The waterway which at one time had been referred to as "Clinton's Ditch" was known now as the "Erie Canal."

More About This Book

WHEN DE WITT CLINTON LIVED

1769   DE WITT CLINTON WAS BORN IN NEW YORK
PROVINCE, MARCH 2.

There were thirteen colonies.

The population of the colonies was about 2,146,000.

1769–   DE WITT LIVED IN NEW BRITAIN AND STUDIED
1783   WITH A TUTOR AND AT AN ACADEMY.

The First Continental Congress met, 1774.

The Declaration of Independence was signed, 1776.

The peace treaty with England was signed, ending the Revolutionary War, 1783.

1784–   DE WITT ATTENDED COLUMBIA COLLEGE
1796   AND BECAME LAWYER AND SECRETARY.

The Constitutional Convention met to frame the United States Constitution, 1787.

George Washington was President, 1789-1797.

Eli Whitney invented the cotton gin, 1793.

| 1797– | CLINTON SERVED AS ASSEMBLYMAN, STATE SEN- |
| 1809 | ATOR, UNITED STATES SENATOR, AND MAYOR. |

The United States bought the Louisiana Territory from France, 1803.

Lewis and Clark explored the Northwest, 1804-1806.

Robert Fulton built the "Clermont," first practical steamboat, 1807.

| 1810 | CLINTON WAS A MEMBER OF THE ERIE CANAL COMMISSION. |

The War of 1812 was fought, 1812-1815.

"The Star-Spangled Banner" was written, 1814.

| 1817 | CLINTON BECAME GOVERNOR OF NEW YORK AND BEGAN WORK ON THE ERIE CANAL. |

Florida was purchased from Spain, 1819.

First steamship crossed the Atlantic, 1819.

| 1825 | CLINTON OPENED THE ERIE CANAL BY TRAVELING FROM LAKE ERIE TO THE ATLANTIC. |

John Elgar built the first iron steamboat in America, 1825.

Colonel J. Stevens operated first American steam engine on private track, 1826.

Slavery abolished in New York state, 1827.

1828   DE WITT CLINTON DIED, FEBRUARY 11.

There were twenty-four states in the Union.

John Quincy Adams was President.

The population of the country was about 12,220,000.

DO YOU REMEMBER?

1. When and where was De Witt Clinton born?
2. Why did Mrs. Clinton not allow De Witt to go alone to his grandmother's house?
3. Why did Thunder Cloud stop De Witt and Charles in the forest?
4. Why was De Witt's father away from home?
5. How did Thunder Cloud repay De Witt's kindness?
6. Why did Charles and De Witt enjoy visiting with Mr. Green at Grandfather Clinton's old house?
7. What important discovery did De Witt make when his dog fell down a large hole?
8. What important news of the country did Mr. Clinton write to the family?
9. Why was Mrs. Clinton sure the British would not pass West Point?

10. Why did Mrs. Clinton take here family to New Windsor to visit?

11. What brave act did De Witt do on the wolf hunt?

12. What were some things De Witt learned about the life of an Indian when visiting Thunder Cloud?

13. Why was De Witt allowed to go to New York City for the evacuation of the British?

14. What college did De Witt enter as the first student to enroll?

15. What were some of the many important political offices De Witt held?

16. Why did De Witt Clinton believe the Erie Canal was very important?

IT'S FUN TO LOOK UP THESE THINGS

1. Who were called Tories in America during the Revolutionary War?

2. What important Indian tribes lived near New York during the Revolutionary War?

3. What were the important forts in New York?

4. What is meant by a "classical education"?

5. What were Colonel James Clinton's achievements for the development of our country?

6. Where and how is lacrosse played today?

7. What were some reasons growth to the western part of the continent was difficult?

8. What were some of the problems faced in building the Erie Canal?

9. How much did it cost to build the Erie Canal?

10. How many vessels use the Erie Canal today?

11. What other canals are on the North American continent and are used today?

INTERESTING THINGS YOU CAN DO

1. Make a papier-maché map of the area covered by the Erie Canal. Show the locks in the canal with card-board or thin wood. Indicate the tributaries which fed into the canal.

2. Draw a map of the thirteen original colonies. Show on the map when, where, and by whom each colony was established.

3. Write an imaginary diary as a member of the Erie Canal Commission on its first trip to study the possibilities of building a canal.

4. Find out the history of Columbia College and obtain pictures of the university today.

OTHER BOOKS YOU MAY ENJOY READING

Erie Canal, The, Samuel Hopkins Adams. Trade Edition, Random House. School Edition, Hale.

George Washington: Boy Leader, Augusta Stevenson. Trade and School Editions, Bobbs-Merrill.

Great Declaration, The, Henry Steele Commager. Bobbs-Merrill.

Molly Pitcher: Girl Patriot, Augusta Stevenson. Trade and School Editions, Bobbs-Merrill.

Panama Canal, The, Bob Considine. Trade Edition, Random House. School Edition, Hale.

We Were There When Washington Won at Yorktown, Earl Schenck Miers. Grosset and Dunlap.

INTERESTING WORDS IN THIS BOOK

aglow (*à* glō′) : bright, excited

anticipation (ăn tĭs′ĭ pā′shŭn) : act of looking forward, especially with pleasure

blocked (blŏkt) : stood in the pathway

bolt (bōlt) : heavy sliding bar or rod used to fasten a door

198

booty (bo͞o′tĭ) : food, prizes, goods taken from an enemy or by thieves

chamber (chām′bĕr) : large space resembling a room

cherished (chĕr′ĭsht) : very important to protect or care for tenderly

clenched (klĕncht) : held together firmly

cocked hat (kŏkt hăt) : hat with large stiff flaps turned up to a peaked crown

compound (kŏm′pound) : enclosure containing a house and buildings needing protection from an enemy attack

dense (dĕns) : closely packed together

eerie (ē′rĭ) : frightening

evacuation (ė văk′ủ ā′shŭn) : withdrawal of troops and population from a town or territory

flushed (flŭsht) : startled into moving suddenly

hazel (hā′z'l) : light, reddish brown color

hew (hū) : cut or chop down as with an ax

hitching post: firmly fixed piece of timber, sometimes with a ring, to which the reins of horses are fastened

indignantly (ĭn dĭg′nănt lĭ) : in an angry manner because of unfair treatment

mope (mōp) : act sad, out-of-spirits, in low mood

mournful (mōrn′f′l) : sad, sorrowful

nuzzled (nŭz′′ld) : rubbed with the nose, lay close

parley (pär′lĭ) : meeting especially with an enemy to discuss terms for peace

pathetic (pȧ thĕt′ĭk) : causing a feeling of pity

pinkster bush (pĭngk′stĕr) : of the pink azalea

post-rider: horseman who carries messages from one station to another along a fixed route

refugee (rĕf′ů jē′) : someone who flees for safety because of political persecution

scurry (skûr′ĭ) : move rapidly along

sedan-carriers (sė dăn′) : men who carry the poles supporting a portable covered chair that holds one person

settle (sĕt′′l) : long wooden bench with arms, a straight high back, and sometimes a boxlike seat

stimulating (stĭm′ů lāt′ĭng) : making more active or exciting

stockade (stŏk ād′) : fence of heavy posts or logs set close together to form a protected enclosure

tethered (tĕth′ĕrd) : fastened with rope or chain so that there are free movements with certain links

wily (wīl′ĭ) : clever, cunning, crafty

Childhood
OF FAMOUS AMERICANS

COLONIAL DAYS

JAMES OGLETHORPE, *Parks*
MYLES STANDISH, *Stevenson*
PETER STUYVESANT, *Widdemer*
POCAHONTAS, *Seymour*
PONTIAC, *Peckham*
SQUANTO, *Stevenson*
VIRGINIA DARE, *Stevenson*
WILLIAM BRADFORD, *Smith*
WILLIAM PENN, *Mason*

STRUGGLE for INDEPENDENCE

ANTHONY WAYNE, *Stevenson*
BEN FRANKLIN, *Stevenson*
BETSY ROSS, *Weil*
DAN MORGAN, *Bryant*
ETHAN ALLEN, *Winders*
FRANCIS MARION, *Steele*
GEORGE ROGERS CLARK, *Wilkie*
GEORGE WASHINGTON, *Stevenson*
ISRAEL PUTNAM, *Stevenson*
JOHN PAUL JONES, *Snow*
JOHN SEVIER, *Steele*
MARTHA WASHINGTON, *Wagoner*
MOLLY PITCHER, *Stevenson*
NATHANAEL GREENE, *Peckham*
NATHAN HALE, *Stevenson*
PATRICK HENRY, *Barton*
PAUL REVERE, *Stevenson*
TOM JEFFERSON, *Monsell*

EARLY NATIONAL GROWTH

ABIGAIL ADAMS, *Wagoner*
ALEC HAMILTON, *Higgins*
ANDY JACKSON, *Stevenson*
DAN WEBSTER, *Smith*
DeWITT CLINTON, *Widdemer*
DOLLY MADISON, *Monsell*
ELIAS HOWE, *Corcoran*
ELI WHITNEY, *Snow*
FRANCIS SCOTT KEY, *Stevenson*
HENRY CLAY, *Monsell*
JAMES FENIMORE COOPER, *Winders*
JAMES MONROE, *Widdemer*
JOHN AUDUBON, *Mason*
JOHN JACOB ASTOR, *Anderson*
JOHN MARSHALL, *Monsell*
JOHN QUINCY ADAMS, *Weil*
LUCRETIA MOTT, *Burnett*
MATTHEW CALBRAITH PERRY, *Scharbach*
NANCY HANKS, *Stevenson*
NOAH WEBSTER, *Higgins*
OLIVER HAZARD PERRY, *Long*
RACHAEL JACKSON, *Govan*
ROBERT FULTON, *Henry*
SAMUEL MORSE, *Snow*
SEQUOYAH, *Snow*
STEPHEN DECATUR, *Smith*
STEPHEN FOSTER, *Higgins*
WASHINGTON IRVING, *Widdemer*
ZACH TAYLOR, *Wilkie*

WESTWARD MOVEMENT

BUFFALO BILL, *Stevenson*
DANIEL BOONE, *Stevenson*
DAVY CROCKETT, *Parks*
JED SMITH, *Burt*
JESSIE FREMONT, *Wagoner*
JIM BOWIE, *Winders*
JIM BRIDGER, *Winders*